Microwave Applications in Chemical Engineering

Microwave Applications in Chemical Engineering

Special Issue Editors

Kama Huang
Junwu Tao
Huacheng Zhu

MDPI • Basel • Beijing • Wuhan • Barcelona • Belgrade • Manchester • Tokyo • Cluj • Tianjin

Special Issue Editors

Kama Huang
Sichuan University
China

Junwu Tao
University of Toulouse
France

Huacheng Zhu
Sichuan University
China

Editorial Office
MDPI
St. Alban-Anlage 66
4052 Basel, Switzerland

This is a reprint of articles from the Special Issue published online in the open access journal *Processes* (ISSN 2227-9717) (available at: https://www.mdpi.com/journal/processes/special_issues/microwave_chemical).

For citation purposes, cite each article independently as indicated on the article page online and as indicated below:

LastName, A.A.; LastName, B.B.; LastName, C.C. Article Title. *Journal Name* **Year**, *Article Number*, Page Range.

ISBN 978-3-03936-495-4 (Hbk)
ISBN 978-3-03936-496-1 (PDF)

Contents

About the Special Issue Editors

Kama Huang was born in Chongqing, China, in 1964. He received his M.S. and Ph.D. degrees in Microwave Theory and Technology from the University of Electronic Science and Technology, Chengdu, China, respectively, in 1988 and 1991. He has been Professor at the Department of Radio and Electronics of Sichuan University, Sichuan, China, since 1994, and Director of the department since 1997. In 1996, 1997, 1999, and 2001, he was respectively Visiting Scientist at the Scientific Research Center "Vidhuk" in Ukraine, Institute of Biophysics CNR in Italy, Technical University Vienna in Austria, and Clemson University in the US. He cooperated with scientists at these institutions to study the interaction between electromagnetic fields and complex media in biological structures and reaction systems. His research interests are in the areas of microwave chemistry and electromagnetic theory.

Junwu Tao: 4GCMEA Technical Program Committee chair. He received his B.Sc. degree in Electronics from the Radio Engineering Department, Huazhong (Central China) University of Science and Technology, Wuhan, China, in 1982; Ph.D. degree (with honors) from the Institut National Polytechnique of Toulouse, France, in 1988; and Habilitation degree from the University of Savoie, France, in 1999. He was conducted research at the electronics laboratory of ENSEEIHT, Toulouse, France, from 1983 to 1991, where he worked on the application of various numerical methods to two- and three-dimensional problems in electromagnetics, as well as the design of microwave and millimeter-wave devices. From 1991 to 2001, he served as Associate Professor in Electrical Engineering at the microwave laboratory (LAHC) at the University of Savoie, Chambéry, France, where he was involved in the full-wave characterization of discontinuity in various planar waveguides and nonlinear transmission line design. Since September 2001, he has held a full position as Professor at the Institut National Polytechnique of Toulouse, where he is involved in computational electromagnetics, multiphysics modeling, design of microwave and RF components, microwave and millimeter-wave measurements, and microwave power applications.

Huacheng Zhu was born in Xuzhou, China, in March 1986. He received his B.Sc. and Ph.D. degrees from Sichuan University in 2009 and 2014, in Electric Engineering and Information and Radio Physics, respectively. From 2015, he has been a faculty member of Sichuan University. During 2012–2013, he was Visiting Fellow at the Department of Biological and Environmental Engineering at Cornell University, Ithaca, USA, which was supported by the China Scholarship Council. His special fields of interest include microwave heating of food, biological tissues, and chemical reactions.

Editorial

Special Issue on "Microwave Applications in Chemical Engineering"

Huacheng Zhu [1,*]**, Kama Huang** [1,*] **and Junwu Tao** [2,*]

1   College of Electronic and Information Engineering, Sichuan University, Chengdu 610065, China
2   LAPLACE, Toulouse INP-ENSEEIHT, University of Toulouse, 31013 Toulouse, France
*   Correspondence: hczhu@scu.edu.cn (H.Z.); kmhuang@scu.edu.cn (K.H.); tao@laplace.univ-tlse.fr (J.T.)

Received: 16 April 2020; Accepted: 17 April 2020; Published: 23 April 2020

Abstract: Microwave heating has been widely used in the chemical industry because of its advantages, such as fast heating rate, selective and controllable heating, increasing reaction rate and reducing by-products in chemical reactions. The Special Issue contains research on microwave applications in chemical engineering.

1. Microwave Equipment and Method Optimization

Microwave-assisted chemical production needs a device that generates microwave energy. The common microwave sources are magnetron and solid-state power generators. Magnetron has the advantages of low cost and high output power, while the solid-state power generator has the characteristics of output power variability and frequency adjustability. In the paper by Mitani et al. [1], a microwave irradiation probe of cylindrical metal applicators for solid microwave heating is designed and studied by using the 3D finite element simulation method. Compared with the traditional system, the designed system helps to reduce the size of the applicator and overall equipment.

Although microwave-assisted processing is widely used, there are still some shortcomings and limitations. When a large number of solid materials are stacked in the microwave applicator, the existence of some sharp edges, tips or submicroscopic irregularities may lead to electric sparks or arcs. In the paper by Wang et al. [2], a method of adding fluid materials with different dielectric constants to solid stacking materials is proposed. The silicon carbide spheres are stacked on the bottom of the quartz cup, and the microwave heating process of water and glycerin as fluid materials is compared by the finite element method. The effects of different permittivity of fluid materials on the heating uniformity were analyzed.

When microwaves act on different materials, sometimes it is necessary to optimize the heating mode according to its characteristics, such as when oleic acid is used in biodiesel production, it needs to be heated before esterification. However, oleic acid is a kind of solution with low dielectric loss and weak absorption capacity for microwave energy, so it is difficult to be directly heated by microwaves. In the paper by Ma et al. [3], a microwave heating model for heating oleic acid was designed: in a quartz tube, oleic acid flows through the porous medium with high dielectric loss, and the porous medium is heated by microwave to indirectly heat the oleic acid. The effects of different flow rate of the oleic acid and porosity of the porous media on microwave heating efficiency were analyzed.

2. Application of Microwave Heating in Material Extraction

In addition to the differences between the materials used in the production of medicinal materials, food and daily necessities, the extraction process also has a significant impact on the product quality. In the extraction of essential oil from plant materials, the common methods are the conventional hydro-distillation method (HD) and the microwave-assisted hydro-distillation (MAHD). Research shows that microwave-assisted extraction can improve the yield and quality of volatile oil. In the paper by Tran et al. [4], the MAHD method was used to extract essential oil from Vietnamese basil, and response surface methodology (RSM) was used to optimize the extraction process from raw material to water ratio, microwave power and extraction time. Based on the analysis of the chemical components of the essential oil extracted from Vietnamese basil, and compared with other studies, the application of Vietnamese basil in the possible large-scale production was proposed. In addition, Bachtler et al. [5] studied and evaluated the extraction kinetics of polyphenols extracted from red vine leaves by using fully automatic laboratory robots and unconventional processing technologies such as ultrasonic (US), microwave (MW) and pulsed electric field (PEF).

In recent years, the application of traditional Chinese medicine has been widely considered. The extraction of healthy compounds from traditional Chinese medicine is an important direction of the development of traditional Chinese medicine, so it is necessary to develop an efficient and simple extraction process. In the paper of He et al. [6], ultrasonic-assisted extraction (UAE) is used to extract antioxidant flavonoids (AFs) from Aurantii fructus (zhiqiao, ZQ). Response surface methodology (RSM) was used to optimize the ethanol concentration, extraction temperature, extraction time and other factors to improve the extraction process of antioxidant flavonoids in ZQ. The suitable extraction conditions of AFs in ZQ were studied. Then, the main components of AFs in ZQ were analyzed by liquid chromatography combined with quadrupole time-of-flight mass spectrometry (LC–Q–TOF–MS).

3. Application of Microwave Heating in Waste Treatment and Drying

The traditional treatment of carbon fiber-reinforced polymer (CFRP) waste is usually by landfill disposal or incineration. At present, a variety of technologies for carbon fiber recovery from carbon fiber reinforced epoxy composites have been proposed. In Deng's paper [7], the degradation of epoxy resin in the CFRP waste and the recycling of carbon fiber were studied by microwave thermolysis and traditional thermolysis respectively. The effects of reaction temperature and reaction time on the recovery of carbon fiber were studied, and the properties of carbon fiber were characterized to compare the characteristics of the two methods.

In view of the problem of the drying treatment of the drill cuttings generated in the drilling operation, in the paper by Tınmaz Köse [8], two drying systems, microwave drying and conveyor belt drying, were used to dry cuttings containing water-based drilling fluid. The differences of drying time and energy consumption between the two drying systems were compared. Zhao et al. [9] studied the thin-layer drying kinetics and mathematical model of Zhaotong lignite under different temperature (100–140 °C) and different microwave power (500–800 W). The effective diffusion coefficient and activation energy of lignite during the drying process were determined.

The above article covers the design and optimization of microwave equipment and some microwave applications in chemical engineering. These studies not only have practical significance, but also have some reference value for the optimization and expansion of microwave applications in the future.

Author Contributions: H.Z. wrote the initial draft of the manuscript; K.H. and J.T. reviewed and contributed to the final manuscript. All authors have read and agreed to the published version of the manuscript.

Funding: There is no funding supports.

Conflicts of Interest: The author declares no conflict of interest.

References

1. Mitani, T.; Nakajima, R.; Shinohara, N.; Nozaki, Y.; Chikata, T.; Watanabe, T. Development of a Microwave Irradiation Probe for a Cylindrical Applicator. *Processes* **2019**, *7*, 143. [CrossRef]
2. Wang, J.; Hong, T.; Xie, T.; Yang, F.; Hu, Y.; Zhu, H. Impact of Filled Materials on the Heating Uniformity and Safety of Microwave Heating Solid Stack Materials. *Processes* **2018**, *6*, 220. [CrossRef]
3. Ma, W.; Hong, T.; Xie, T.; Wang, F.; Luo, B.; Zhou, J.; Yang, Y.; Zhu, H.; Huang, K. Simulation and Analysis of Oleic Acid Pretreatment for Microwave-Assisted Biodiesel Production. *Processes* **2018**, *6*, 142. [CrossRef]

4. Tran, T.H.; Nguyen, H.H.H.; Nguyen, T.D.; Nguyen, T.Q.; Tan, H.; Nhan, L.H.; Nguyen, D.H.; Tran, D.L.; Do, S.T.; Nguyen, T.D. Optimization of Microwave-Assisted Extraction of Essential Oil from Vietnamese Basil (Ocimum basilicum L.) Using Response Surface Methodology. *Processes* **2018**, *6*, 206. [CrossRef]
5. Bachtler, S.; Attarakih, M. Polyphenols from Red Vine Leaves Using Alternative Processing Techniques. *Processes* **2018**, *6*, 262. [CrossRef]
6. He, Y.; Chen, Y.; Shi, Y.; Zhao, K.; Tan, H.; Zeng, J.; Tang, Q.; Xie, H. Multiresponse Optimization of Ultrasonic-Assisted Extraction for Aurantii Fructus to Obtain High Yield of Antioxidant Flavonoids Using a Response Surface Methodology. *Processes* **2018**, *6*, 258. [CrossRef]
7. Deng, J.; Xu, L.; Zhang, L.; Peng, J.; Guo, S.; Liu, J.; Koppala, S. Recycling of Carbon Fibers from CFRP Waste by Microwave Thermolysis. *Processes* **2019**, *7*, 207. [CrossRef]
8. Köse, E.T. Drying of Drill Cuttings: Emphasis on Energy Consumption and Thermal Analysis. *Processes* **2019**, *7*, 145. [CrossRef]
9. Zhao, P.; Liu, C.; Qu, W.; He, Z.; Gao, J.; Jia, L.; Ji, S.; Ruan, R. Effect of Temperature and Microwave Power Levels on Microwave Drying Kinetics of Zhaotong Lignite. *Processes* **2019**, *7*, 74. [CrossRef]

Article

Development of a Microwave Irradiation Probe for a Cylindrical Applicator

Tomohiko Mitani [1,*], Ryo Nakajima [1], Naoki Shinohara [1], Yoshihiro Nozaki [2], Tsukasa Chikata [2] and Takashi Watanabe [1]

[1]   Research Institute for Sustainable Humanosphere, Kyoto University, Kyoto 611-0011, Japan;
    ryo_nakajima@rish.kyoto-u.ac.jp (R.N.); shino@rish.kyoto-u.ac.jp (N.S.); twatanab@rish.kyoto-u.ac.jp (T.W.)
[2]   Japan Chemical Engineering & Machinery Co. Ltd., Osaka 532-0031, Japan; y-nozaki@nikkaki.co.jp (Y.N.);
    chikata9366@gmail.com (T.C.)
*   Correspondence: mitani@rish.kyoto-u.ac.jp; Tel.: +81-774-38-3880

Received: 25 January 2019; Accepted: 5 March 2019; Published: 7 March 2019

Abstract: A microwave irradiation probe was newly developed for downsizing microwave applicators and the overall microwave heating apparatus. The key component of the proposed probe is a tapered section composed of polytetrafluoroethylene (PTFE) and alumina. Insertion of the tapered section between the input port and the applicator vessel realizes impedance matching to the microwave power source and reduces the reflected power from the applicator. The proposed microwave probe for a cylindrical applicator was designed using 3D electromagnetic simulations. The permittivity data of two liquid samples—ultrapure water and 2 M NaOH solution—were measured and taken into simulations. The conductivity of the NaOH solution was estimated from the measurement results. The measured reflection ratio of the fabricated applicator was in good accordance with the simulated one. The frequency ranges in which the measured reflection ratio was less than 10% were from 1.45 GHz to 2.7 GHz when using water and from 1.6 GHz to 2.7 GHz when using the NaOH solution as the sample. The heating rate of the applicator was roughly estimated as 63 to 69 K for a 5 min interval during the 2.45 GHz microwave irradiation at the input power of 100 W.

Keywords: microwave heating; applicator design; electromagnetic simulation; coaxial feeding

---

1. Introduction

Applications of microwave heating and microwave irradiation to chemical reactions covering a wide variety of research fields have been reported over the past three decades [1–9]. Various concepts of microwave irradiation methods have been introduced [3], and in most cases, a single-mode cavity and a multi-mode cavity, such as a microwave oven, have been used for the microwave heating applications. Recently, continuous-flow systems have been well studied [1] because the penetration depth of the microwave at 2.45 GHz, which is allocated in the industrial, scientific, and medical (ISM) bands, limits the applicator size of microwave heating. Downsizing the applicator will, therefore, prevail in future microwave heating applications. A number of types of small diameter micro-flow applicators have already been reported [10–13].

Another trend in microwave heating applications is the replacement of the microwave power source. Since the early days of microwave heating, a vacuum tube device called a magnetron [14] has been used as the microwave power source and has also been widely used in microwave ovens. However, high-power solid-state devices are attracting a great deal of attention as an alternative microwave power source due to their variability in output power, adjustability in frequency, and easy operability. Moreover, the solid-state generators can set the frequency precisely and be adjustable with high purity and a narrow bandwidth of frequency spectrum. Although the magnetron is still superior to the solid-state device with respect to cost and maximum output power, the development of solid-state microwave power amplifiers, 1 kW in the 2.45-GHz band [15] and 64 kW in the 915-MHz band [16], were recently commercialized. A number of studies on microwave heating using solid-state devices have also been reported [17–20]. Our group has previously developed a wideband microwave applicator with a coaxial cable structure [21], based on using solid-state devices.

The objective of the present study is to develop a microwave irradiation probe for a cylindrical metal applicator for microwave heating by solid-state devices. In most conventional applicators for microwave chemistry, heated liquid samples were put in a material transparent to microwaves, such as glass [22] or polymer [23]. As a metal resonant cavity and waveguides were used in these types of applicators, the overall microwave heating apparatus became large. The novelty of the proposed system is direct microwave irradiation of a liquid sample in a metal vessel; it also contributes to downsizing the applicator and the overall apparatus compared to the conventional systems. The proposed microwave probe for a cylindrical applicator was designed using 3D electromagnetic simulations based on the finite element method (FEM), which is commonly available and is used in applicator design [24,25].

2. Materials and Methods

2.1. Overview of the Proposed Microwave Irradiation Probe and Cylindrical Applicator

A cross-sectional schematic of the proposed microwave irradiation probe and the cylindrical applicator is shown in Figure 1. The applicator is a cylindrical vessel made of SUS 316L non-magnetic stainless steel. Microwaves are radiated to the liquid samples from the side of the vessel. A pressure gauge is attached to the top of the applicator to maintain the internal pressure. The microwave irradiation port consists of a commercially available Type-N connector with a characteristic impedance of 50 Ω. In this applicator design, a magnetic stir bar, which can stir liquid samples, can be placed on the bottom of the vessel.

As a feature of the proposed microwave irradiation probe, a tapered section is inserted between the input port and the vessel to realize impedance matching to the microwave power source and to reduce the reflected power from the applicator. This section is composed of polytetrafluoroethylene (PTFE) and alumina. A concave PTFE component is inserted from the microwave input side, and a convex alumina component is inserted from the applicator side. These parts are embedded in the coaxial section, and the inner conductor passes through them. A stainless-steel cylindrical block, called a supporter, is placed at the end of the alumina block to support the inner conductor and the alumina. The supporter also plays a role in preventing the PTFE from varying its length by thermal expansion during microwave heating.

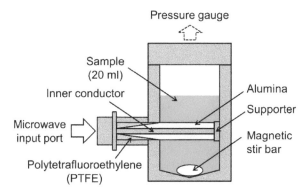

Figure 1. Cross-sectional schematic of the proposed microwave irradiation probe and cylindrical applicator. The applicator is made of stainless-steel (SUS 316L). Microwaves are radiated to the liquid samples from the side of the vessel.

2.2. Liquid Samples and Permittivity Measurements

Two liquid samples were selected for designing the applicator: ultrapure water (hereinafter water) as a dielectric sample and 2 M NaOH solution (hereinafter NaOH solution) as a dielectric and conductive sample. The water was obtained from an ultrapure water system (PURELAB Flex3 PF3XXXXM1, ELGA, High Wycombe, UK) and had an electrical resistivity greater than 18 MΩ·cm. The NaOH solution was obtained by dissolving NaOH (JIS Special Grade, Wako Pure Chemical Industries, Ltd., Osaka, Japan) in the same water.

Permittivity measurements of the two liquid samples were conducted using the coaxial probe method [26]. The liquid sample was placed in a glass bottle, and a slim form probe (85070E, Agilent, Santa Rosa, CA, USA) was immersed in the sample. The reflection coefficient at the boundary between the sample and the probe was measured by a network analyzer (N5242A, Agilent, Santa Rosa, CA, USA), and the relative complex permittivity $\varepsilon = \varepsilon' - j\varepsilon''$ was calculated over the frequency range from 500 MHz to 20 GHz, where j, ε' and ε'' are the imaginary unit, the real and imaginary parts of the relative permittivity, respectively. Permittivity measurements were repeated three times at room temperature.

Note that the imaginary part of the measured relative permittivity ε''_m includes the conductivity σ with this measurement method, as expressed by the following equation:

$$\varepsilon''_m = \varepsilon'' + \sigma/(2\pi f \varepsilon_0), \tag{1}$$

where ε_0 and f are the permittivity in a vacuum and the frequency, respectively. The conductivity of the water can be regarded as 0; however, the conductivity of the NaOH solution cannot be ignored when designing the cylindrical applicator with the microwave irradiation probe by electromagnetic simulations precisely. Therefore, we estimated the conductivity σ by fitting the inverse proportional curve obtained in the low frequency range in which the effects of ε'' are negligible compared to σ. Then, the approximate equation of σ in the low frequency range is expressed as follows:

$$\sigma \approx 2\pi f \varepsilon_0 \varepsilon''_m. \tag{2}$$

With respect to the water, the measured permittivity data were compared with the Debye relaxation model, as expressed in the following equation:

$$\varepsilon = \varepsilon_\infty + \frac{\varepsilon_s - \varepsilon_\infty}{1 + j2\pi f\tau}, \tag{3}$$

where ε_∞, ε_s and τ are ε' at sufficiently high frequency, ε' at sufficiently low frequency and the Debye relaxation time [27]. The parameters of ε_∞, ε_s and τ were obtained from the reference [28]; $\varepsilon_\infty = 5.2$, $\varepsilon_s = 78.36$, and $\tau = 8.27$ ps at a temperature of 25 °C.

2.3. Design of the Proposed Microwave Irradiation Probe and Cylindrical Applicator

The proposed microwave irradiation probe and cylindrical applicator were designed with the aid of the 3D electromagnetic simulation software package (HFSS ver 19.0, ANSYS, Canonsburg, PA, USA), which calculates the reflection coefficient, S_{11}, for the input microwave port that is defined as the element of the scattering matrix in a one-port network circuit [29].

Simulation models of the applicator are shown in Figure 2. The general simulation setup involved frequencies ranging from 80 MHz to 2.7 GHz with an input microwave power of 100 W. The target frequency in the simulations was 2.45 GHz. The values for the real part of the relative permittivity ε' and the dielectric loss tangent $\tan \delta = \varepsilon''/\varepsilon'$ were 2.08 and 0.001 for the PTFE, and 9.4 and 0.006 for the alumina. The conductivity of the SUS 316L was 1.1×10^6 S/m. The parameters of the PTFE, alumina, and SUS 316L were obtained from the library data in the simulation software. The volume of the liquid sample, either water or the NaOH solution, set in the applicator was 20 mL. The measured relative permittivity and conductivity of the liquid samples were imported into the simulation software. A magnetic stir bar was not taken into account in the simulations. The simulation parameters are summarized in Table 1. The mesh for the simulations was created by using the function of adaptive auto mesh in the simulation software.

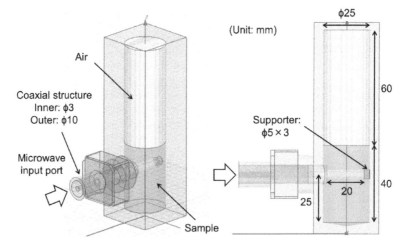

Figure 2. Simulation model of the cylindrical applicator with the microwave irradiation probe.

Table 1. Simulation parameters.

Parameters	Values
Target frequency	2.45 GHz
Start frequency	80 MHz
Stop frequency	2.7 GHz
Input power	100 W
Number of mesh	19,236 (water), 15,674 (NaOH solution)
Permittivity of PTFE	2.08–j 0.00208
Permittivity of alumina	9.4–j 0.0564
Conductivity of SUS 316L	1.1×10^6 S/m

Figure 3 shows the designed and fabricated cylindrical applicator with the microwave irradiation probe. The optical fiber thermometer port was attached orthogonally to the microwave input port on the side of the applicator. The pressure gauge can be removed from the applicator to pour in the liquid sample. The maximum temperature and inner pressure were designed to be 200 °C and 2 MPa, respectively.

Microwave input port   Pressure gauge

Optical fiber thermometer port

Figure 3. Photographs of the developed cylindrical applicator with the microwave irradiation probe. The optical fiber thermometer port was attached orthogonally to the microwave input port on the side of the applicator. The pressure gauge was mounted to the top of the applicator to maintain the internal pressure.

2.4. Microwave Reflection Measurements for the Cylindrical Applicator

The reflection coefficient of the microwaves at the input port of the applicator, S_{11}, was measured using a network analyzer (Agilent N5242A). The absolute value of S_{11} was converted to the reflection ratio R, which is the ratio of the input power to the reflected power, by the following equation:

$$R = 100\% \times |S_{11}|. \tag{4}$$

A 20 mL aliquot of the liquid sample, either the water or the NaOH solution, was poured into the applicator, and microwave reflection measurements were executed at room temperature.

2.5. Microwave Heating Tests

A diagram of the microwave heating measurement system is shown in Figure 4. A 20 mL aliquot of the liquid sample was poured into the applicator and stirred during the microwave heating. Microwaves were generated using a signal generator (Agilent N5183A), amplified by a solid-state power amplifier (R&K GA0827-4754-R), and input to the applicator through a coaxial cable. The input power P_i and the reflected power P_r were monitored by a power meter (Agilent E4417A) through power sensors (Agilent N8485A). Here, P_i was fixed at 100 W during the microwave heating tests. The sample temperature T was measured using a fiber optic thermometer (ANRITSU FL-2400). Although a single-point measurement cannot verify the temperature uniformity of the liquid sample even if it is stirred, the measured temperature was used as a representative of sample temperature in this study, due to the limitation of temperature measurements in the applicator. The values of P_i, P_r, and T were logged at one-second intervals using a data logger (GRAPHTEC GL800). The microwave heating tests were conducted at frequencies of 1.7 GHz and 2.45 GHz. The microwaves were stopped when the measured temperature reached 100 °C. The reflection ratio R defined by Equation (1) was also obtained as the ratio between P_i and P_r as follows:

$$R = 100\% \times P_r / P_i. \tag{5}$$

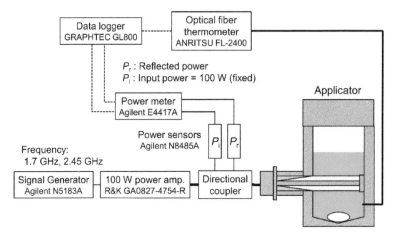

Figure 4. Diagram of the microwave heating measurement system.

3. Results

Figure 5 shows the measured average permittivity of two liquid samples. When the average permittivity data were regarded as the true permittivity, the measurement errors were less than 1.4% in the water case and less than 1.0% in the NaOH case. Note that the measured data for the NaOH solution in Figure 5b represents the apparent imaginary part of the relative permittivity because they include the conductivity of the solution.

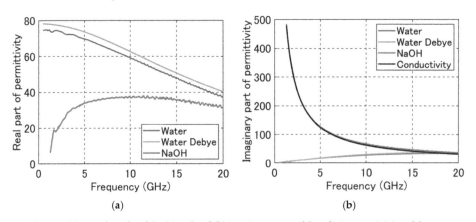

Figure 5. Measured results of the (**a**) real and (**b**) imaginary parts of the relative permittivity of the two different liquid samples. The average values of three measurements are plotted. The green lines plot the permittivity of the Debye relaxation model [28]. The black line in (**b**) plots the curve of $\sigma / (2\pi f \varepsilon_0)$ at the conductivity σ of 34.7 S/m.

Figure 6 plots the simulated and measured reflection ratios for the applicators using either water or the NaOH solution as samples. Figures 7 and 8 show simulation results for the electric field distribution and the absorbed power distribution, respectively, in the applicator at 2.45 GHz. The absorbed power distribution was obtained by using the calculation function of the specific absorption ratio (SAR) in the HFSS software and was normalized by the material density.

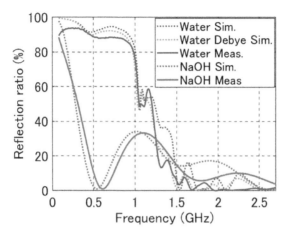

Figure 6. Simulated and measured results of the reflection ratios for the developed cylindrical applicator using liquid samples of water and a NaOH solution.

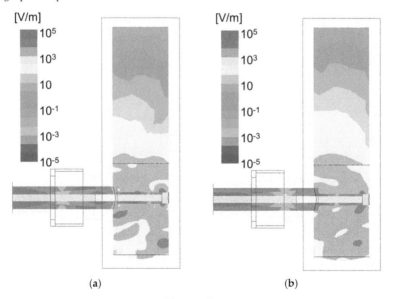

(a)   (b)

Figure 7. *Cont.*

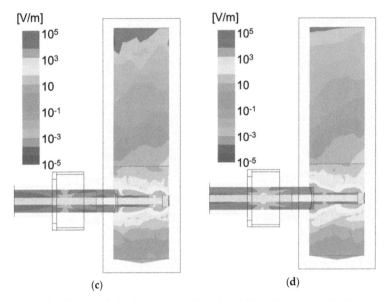

(c)   (d)

Figure 7. Simulated electric field distribution in the cylindrical applicator using liquid samples of water at (**a**) 2.45 GHz and (**b**) 1.7 GHz, and a NaOH solution at (**c**) 2.45 GHz and (**d**) 1.7 GHz.

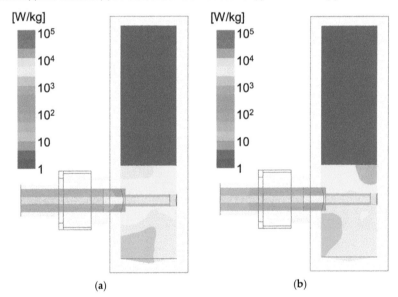

(a)   (b)

Figure 8. *Cont.*

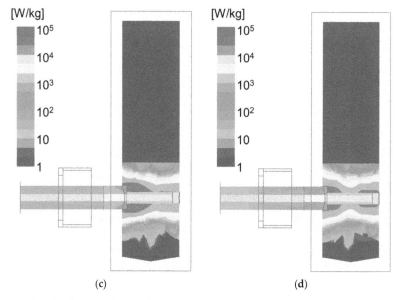

(c)   (d)

Figure 8. Simulated absorbed power distribution in the cylindrical applicator using liquid samples of water at (**a**) 2.45 GHz and (**b**) 1.7 GHz, and a NaOH solution at (**c**) 2.45 GHz and (**d**) 1.7 GHz.

Figure 9 summarizes the temperature increases observed during the microwave heating trials using water or a NaOH solution. Figure 10 shows the experimental results for the reflection ratio during the microwave heating tests.

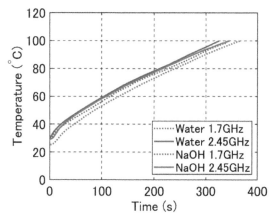

Figure 9. Measured results of temperature increases using water and a NaOH solution during microwave heating.

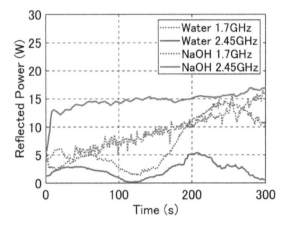

Figure 10. Reflected power of the developed cylindrical applicator during microwave heating.

4. Discussion

4.1. Estimation of the Conductivity and Permittivity

The estimated conductivity of the NaOH solution, which was calculated from Equation (2), is plotted in Figure 11. As it includes the term $2\pi f \varepsilon_0 \varepsilon''$ by substituting Equation (1) into Equation (2), the estimated conductivity increases in frequency in the high frequency range. From Figure 11, we adopted the minimum value of the estimated conductivity of 34.7 S/m as the conductivity of the NaOH solution in the simulations, in order to avoid that ε'' becomes negative in the permittivity estimation. The curve of $\sigma/(2\pi f \varepsilon_0)$ at $\sigma = 34.7$ S/m was overplotted as the black line in Figure 5b. It was found, from the comparison between the measured data and the overplotted curve, that the measured imaginary part of relative permittivity for the NaOH solution was almost influenced by the conductivity.

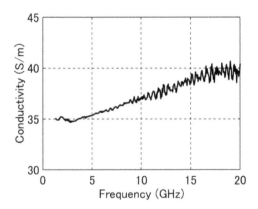

Figure 11. Estimated conductivity of the NaOH solution calculated by Equation (2).

Figure 12 shows the estimated imaginary part of the relative permittivity for the NaOH solution, which was calculated from Equation (1). The measured ε'' for the water, whose conductivity was not taken into account, is also plotted. From the measured and estimated results of Figures 5a, 11 and 12, the values of relative permittivity and conductivity taken into the simulation model at 2.45 GHz are summarized in Table 2.

By comparison of the measurement results of water with the Debye relaxation model, the measurement errors of permittivity ranged from −3.7% to −8.4% for the real part, and from 15.2% to −14.5% for the imaginary part when the model parameters described in Section 2.2 were adopted as the true value. As the errors were not negligibly small, the electromagnetic simulations for the water were conducted by using the Debye relaxation model as well as the measured permittivity. The relative permittivity of the Debye relaxation model at 2.45 GHz is also summarized in Table 2.

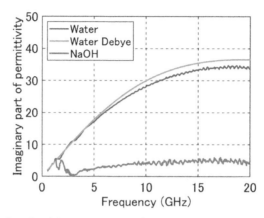

Figure 12. Estimated results of the imaginary part of the relative permittivity for the NaOH solution. The conductivity of the NaOH solution was set to 34.7 S/m. The conductivity effect was not taken into account for the water.

Table 2. The relative permittivity and conductivity were taken into the simulation model at 2.45 GHz.

Sample	Relative Permittivity	Conductivity (S/m)
Water	74.0–j 9.4	0
Water (Debye, 25 °C) [28]	77.2–j 9.2	0
NaOH solution	22.5–j 2.2	34.7

4.2. Reflection Ratio and Heating Rate of the Developed Applicator

The measurement results for the reflection ratio were in good accordance with the simulation results, as shown in Figure 6. Moreover, the simulation results of the reflection ratios for water when using the Debye relaxation model were in close accordance with those when using the measured permittivity data. The frequency ranges in which the reflection ratio was less than 10% were from 1.45 GHz to 2.7 GHz when using water as the sample and from 1.6 GHz to 2.7 GHz when using the NaOH solution as the sample. The reflection ratio in frequency is dependent on the applicator size and the destructive interference effect inside the liquid sample. Since the diameter of the developed applicator is 25 mm, as shown in Figure 2, the microwaves below 1.45 GHz return to the input port before being propagated and absorbed in the sample.

The electric field and absorbed power distributions in the applicator were relatively uniform in the water case; however, they were focused around the inner conductor in the applicator in the NaOH solution case, as shown in Figures 7 and 8. This indicates that microwaves are well absorbed around the inner conductor due to the conductivity of the NaOH solution. This implies that temperature gradients would take place in the applicator even though the liquid sample was stirred during microwave heating.

Based on the microwave heating results in Figure 9, the heating rate was roughly estimated as 63 to 69 K for a 5 min interval. During the microwave heating trials, the reflected power was less than 17 W, which is equivalent to less than 17% of the reflection ratio, until the time when the samples reached 100 °C and was gradually increased as the sample temperature increased, as shown in Figure 10. It was reported that the real part of the relative permittivity for the water decreases in temperature [21]. Hence, the reflection ratio increased with heating time as the destructive interference effect inside the liquid sample was enhanced.

The similarity of heating rates shown in Figure 9 was mainly attributed to thermal dissipation from the applicator, in spite of the fact that the reflected power was varied in time and temperature as shown in Figure 10. The developed applicator was not insulated against outer air during the microwave heating tests so that thermal radiation from the applicator occurred at higher temperatures. In addition, thermal conduction occurred from the applicator through the coaxial cable. These thermal dissipation effects would lead to the similarity of temperature increases shown in Figure 9.

Regarding the water, the measurement results of reflected power shown in Figure 10 was compared with simulations at temperatures of 30 °C, 40 °C, 50 °C, and 60 °C. The permittivity of the Debye relaxation model [27] was taken into simulations. The parameters for the Debye relaxation model were obtained from Ref. [28]. The comparison results are summarized in Table 3. The measurement results are comparable with simulations at a temperature of 30 °C, immediately after the start of microwave irradiation; however, the measurement results are smaller than the simulations above 40 °C. This is mainly due to temperature non-uniformity in the applicator. Although the magnetic stirrer was used during microwave heating, temperature non-uniformity would still exist. In addition, numerical simulations are usually much more sensitive than measurements.

Table 3. Comparison of reflected power for the water between simulations and measurements.

Frequency (GHz)	Temperature (°C)	Simulation (W)	Measurement (W)
	30	2.2	3.9
	40	8.7	3.8
1.7	50	16.5	4.4
	60	17.9	1.9
	30	2.2	1.3
	40	4.0	2.7
2.45	50	5.1	2.6
	60	8.6	0.7

5. Conclusions

A microwave irradiation probe for a cylindrical metal applicator was designed and fabricated. The newly developed microwave irradiation probe enables downsizing of the applicator and microwave heating apparatus. The coaxial microwave feeding provides high compatibility with solid-state microwave power amplifiers. Furthermore, the developed microwave irradiation method can be applied to a continuous flow applicator [1] by removing the top and bottom metal shields. The developed applicator will be used for producing high-value added chemicals, for example, production of vanillin from wood particles [30]. Although a magnetic stirrer was used in the developed applicator, the developed applicator should be improved from the viewpoint of temperature uniformity in the liquid sample. Coupled analyses using heat equation and hydrodynamic considerations will provide more precise results, including thermal conduction and thermal dissipation, and will contribute to optimization of the present applicator.

Author Contributions: Conceptualization, T.M.; Methodology, T.M., R.N., Y.N., and T.C.; Software, R.N.; Validation, T.M., R.N., N.S., Y.N., T.C., and T.W.; Formal Analysis, T.M., R.N., and N.S.; Investigation, T.M., R.N., Y.N., and T.C.; Resources, Y.N., T.C., and T.W.; Data Curation, T.M., and N.S.; Writing—Original Draft Preparation, T.M.; Writing—Review and Editing, T.M., N.S., and T.W.; Visualization, T.M., and R.N.; Supervision, N.S., and T.W.; Project Administration, T.W.; Funding Acquisition, T.M. and T.W.

Funding: This research was funded by CREST Grant Number 1103784, JST, and JSPS Kakenhi Grant Number JP18K04263.

Acknowledgments: Measurements of the reflection ratios and the microwave heating tests were conducted through the collaborative research program, Analysis and Development System for Advanced Materials (ADAM), at the Research Institute for Sustainable Humanosphere, Kyoto University.

Conflicts of Interest: The authors declare no conflict of interest.

References

1. Estel, L.; Poux, M.; Benamara, N.; Polaert, I. Continuous flow-microwave reactor: Where are we? *Chem. Eng. Process. Process Intensif.* **2017**, *113*, 56–64. [CrossRef]
2. Tung, T.T.; Alotaibi, F.; Nine, M.J.; Silva, R.; Tran, D.N.H.; Janowska, I.; Losic, D. Engineering of highly conductive and ultra-thin nitrogen-doped graphene films by combined methods of microwave irradiation, ultrasonic spraying and thermal annealing. *Chem. Eng. J.* **2018**, *338*, 764–773. [CrossRef]
3. Beneroso, D.; Monti, T.; Kostas, E.T.; Robinson, J. Microwave pyrolysis of biomass for bio-oil production: Scalable processing concepts. *Chem. Eng. J.* **2017**, *316*, 481–498. [CrossRef]
4. Aguilar-Reynosa, A.; Romaní, A.; Rodríguez-Jasso, R.M.; Aguilar, C.N.; Garrote, G.; Ruiz, H.A. Microwave heating processing as alternative of pretreatment in second-generation biorefinery: An overview. *Energy Convers. Manag.* **2017**, *136*, 50–65. [CrossRef]
5. Li, H.; Qu, Y.; Yang, Y.; Chang, S.; Xu, J. Microwave irradiation—A green and efficient way to pretreat biomass. *Bioresour. Technol.* **2017**, *122*, 53–73. [CrossRef] [PubMed]
6. Guo, Q.; Sun, D.; Cheng, J.; Han, Z. Microwave processing techniques and their recent applications in the food industry. *Trends Food Sci. Technol.* **2017**, *67*, 236–247. [CrossRef]
7. McKinstry, C.; Cussen, E.J.; Fletcher, A.J.; Patwardhan, S.V.; Sefcik, J. Scalable continuous production of high quality HKUST-1 via conventional and microwave heating. *Chem. Eng. J.* **2017**, *326*, 570–577. [CrossRef]
8. Wang, N.; Wang, P. Study and application status of microwave in organic wastewater treatment—A review. *Chem. Eng. J.* **2016**, *283*, 193–214. [CrossRef]
9. Rybakov, K.I.; Olevsky, E.A.; Krikun, E.V. Microwave sintering: Fundamentals and modeling. *J. Am. Ceram. Sci.* **2013**, *96*, 1003–1020. [CrossRef]
10. Yin, S.; Chen, K.; Srinivasakannan, C.; Guo, S.; Li, S.; Peng, J.; Zhang, L. Enhancing recovery of ammonia from rare earth wastewater by air stripping combination of microwave heating and high gravity technology. *Chem. Eng. J.* **2018**, *337*, 515–521. [CrossRef]
11. He, W.; Fang, Z.; Zhang, K.; Tu, T.; Lv, N.; Qiu, C.; Guo, K. A novel micro-flow system under microwave irradiation for continuous synthesis of 1,4-dihydropyridines in the absence of solvents via Hantzsch reaction. *Chem. Eng. J.* **2018**, *331*, 161–168. [CrossRef]
12. Garagalza, O.; Petit, C.; Mignard, E.; Sarrazin, F.; Reynaud, S.; Grassl, B. Droplet-based millifluidic device under microwave irradiation: Temperature measurement and polymer particle synthesis. *Chem. Eng. J.* **2017**, *308*, 1105–1111. [CrossRef]
13. Sturm, G.S.J.; Verweij, M.D.; Stankiewicz, A.I.; Stefanidis, G.D. Microwaves and microreactors: Design challenges and remedies. *Chem. Eng. J.* **2014**, *243*, 147–158. [CrossRef]
14. Sivan, L. Magnetron—Detailed principle of operation. In *Microwave Tube Transmitters*; Chapman & Hall: London, UK, 1994; pp. 155–193.
15. Williams, R.; Lindseth, B. Compact 1 kW 2.45 GHz solid-state source for in industrial applications. In Proceedings of the 50th Annual Microwave Power Symposium, Orlando, FL, USA, 21–23 June 2016; pp. 39–41.
16. Bartola, B.; Kaplan, K.; Williams, R. 64 kW microwave generator using LDMOS power amplifiers for industrial heating applications. In Proceedings of the 50th Annual Microwave Power Symposium, Orlando, FL, USA, 21–23 June 2016; pp. 37–38.
17. Wang, K.; Dimistrakis, G.; Irvine, D.J. Exemplification of catalyst design for microwave selective heating and its application to efficient in situ catalyst synthesis. *Chem. Eng. Process. Process Intensif.* **2017**, *122*, 389–396. [CrossRef]
18. Bianchi, C.; Bonato, P.; Dughiero, F.; Canu, P. Enhanced power density uniformity for microwave catalytic reactions adopting solid-state generators: Comparison with magnetron technology. *Chem. Eng. Process. Process Intensif.* **2017**, *120*, 286–300. [CrossRef]

19. Kapranov, S.V.; Kouzaev, G.A. Models of water, methanol, and ethanol and their applications in the design of miniature microwave heating reactors. *Int. J. Therm. Sci.* **2017**, *122*, 53–73. [CrossRef]

20. Sumi, T.; Horikoshi, S. Microwave selective heating for size effect of water droplet in W/O emulsion with sorbitan fatty acid monostearate surfactant. *Radiat. Phys. Chem.* **2015**, *114*, 31–37. [CrossRef]

21. Mitani, T.; Hasegawa, N.; Nakajima, R.; Shinohara, N.; Nozaki, Y.; Chikata, T.; Watanabe, T. Development of a wideband microwave reactor with a coaxial cable structure. *Chem. Eng. J.* **2016**, *299*, 209–216. [CrossRef]

22. Yokozawa, S.; Ohneda, N.; Muramatsu, K.; Okamoto, T.; Odajima, H.; Ikawa, T.; Sugiyama, J.; Fujita, M.; Sawairi, T.; Egami, H.; et al. Development of a highly efficient single-mode microwave reacttor with a resonant cavity and its application to continuous flow syntheses. *RSC Adv.* **2015**, *5*, 10204–10210. [CrossRef]

23. Nishioka, M.; Miyakawa, M.; Kataoka, H.; Koda, H.; Sato, K.; Suzuki, T.M. Continuous synthesis of monodispersed silver nanoparticles using a homogeneous heating microwave reactor system. *Nanoscale* **2011**, *3*, 2621–2626. [CrossRef] [PubMed]

24. Arshanista, A.; Akishin, Y.; Zile, E.; Dizhbite, T.; Solovnik, V.; Telysheva, G. Microwave treatment combined with conventional heating of plant biomass pellets in a rotated reactor as a high rate process for solid biofuel manufacture. *Renew. Energy* **2016**, *91*, 386–396. [CrossRef]

25. Hong, Y.; Lin, B.; Li, H.; Dai, H.; Zhu, C.; Yao, H. Three-dimensional simulation of microwave heating coal sample with varying parameters. *Appl. Therm. Eng.* **2016**, *93*, 1145–1154. [CrossRef]

26. Blackham, D.V.; Pollard, R.D. An improved technique for permittivity measurements using a coaxial probe. *IEEE Trans. Instrum. Meas.* **1997**, *46*, 1093–1099. [CrossRef]

27. Kremer, F.; Schönhals, A. Analysis of Dielectric Spectra. In *Broadband Dielectric Spectroscopy*; Springer: Heidelberg, Germany, 2003; pp. 59–98.

28. Kaatze, U. Complex permittivity of water as a function of frequency and temperature. *J. Chem. Eng. Data* **1989**, *34*, 371–374. [CrossRef]

29. Pozer, D.M. Microwave network analysis. In *Microwave Engineering*, 4th ed.; John Wiley & Sons Inc.: Hoboken, NJ, USA, 2012; pp. 165–227.

30. Qu, C.; Kaneko, M.; Kashimura, K.; Tanaka, K.; Ozawa, S.; Watanabe, T. Direct production of vanillin from wood particles by copper oxide-peroxide reaction promoted by electric and magnetic fields of microwaves. *ACS Sustain. Chem. Eng.* **2017**, *5*, 11551–11557. [CrossRef]

Article

Impact of Filled Materials on the Heating Uniformity and Safety of Microwave Heating Solid Stack Materials

Jing Wang [1], Tao Hong [2,*], Tian Xie [3], Fan Yang [3], Yusong Hu [2] and Huacheng Zhu [1]

[1] College of Electronics and Information Engineering, Sichuan University, Chengdu 610065, China; jwang@stu.scu.edu.cn (J.W.); hczhu@scu.edu.cn (H.Z.)
[2] School of Electronic Information Engineering, China West Normal University, Nanchong 637002, China; yshu1989@163.com
[3] State Key Laboratory of Efficient Utilization for Low Grade Phosphate Rock and Its Associated Resources, Wengfu Group, Guiyang 550014, China; xietian@wengfu.com (T.X.); yangfan@wengfu.com (F.Y.)
* Correspondence: scu_mandela@163.com; Tel.: +86-158-8246-5675

Received: 16 October 2018; Accepted: 29 October 2018; Published: 7 November 2018

Abstract: Microwave heating of solid stack materials is common but bothered by problems of uneven heating and electric discharge phenomena. In this paper, a method introducing fluid materials with different relative permittivity is proposed to improve the heating uniformity and safety of solid stack materials. Simulations have been computed based on the finite element method (FEM) and validated by experiments. Simulation results show that the introducing of fluid materials with proper relative permittivity does improve the heating uniformity and safety. Fluid materials with the larger real part of relative permittivity could obviously lower the maximum modulus value of the electric field for about 23 times, and will lower the coefficient of variation (COV) in general, although in small ranges that it has fluctuated. Fluid materials with the larger imaginary part of relative permittivity, in a range from 0 to 0.3, can make a more efficient heating and it could lower the maximum modulus value of the electric field by 34 to 55% on the whole studied range. However, the larger imaginary part of relative permittivity will cause worse heating uniformity as the COV rises by 246.9% in the same process. The computed results are discussed and methods to reach uniform and safe heating through introducing fluid materials with proper relative permittivity are proposed.

Keywords: microwave heating; uniformity analysis; electric discharge analysis

---

1. Introduction

Unlike traditional heating methods that heat materials by radiation, convection and conduction, microwaves heat materials through the direct interaction with the inner polar molecules and charged particles of materials [1]. Thus, characterized as efficient heating, volumetric heating and selective heating [2–6], microwave heating has been rapidly developed and applied in various areas.

However, there are also some natural drawbacks of microwave heating: (a) When heating materials by microwave, there exist "hot spots" and thermal runaway problems in the system temperature [7], which will cause degradation of the processing materials [8–11] and even cause burning and explosion of the microwave reactor and reactants [12,13]. (b) When dealing with numerous solid materials, their stacking in the heating cavity can easily result in some sharp edges, tips or submicroscopic irregularities, which may lead to electric sparks or electric arcs [14,15]. These electric discharges will affect the heating process and the product composition, and lead to safety problems when dealing with materials that have a low flashing point or in high temperature conditions [16,17].

For studies on microwave heating uniformity improvement, the common methods could be categorized into two aspects [18]: (1) To improve the uniformity of the electromagnetic field in the microwave cavity, such as optimization of microwave power feeding situations [19–22], introducing of mode stirrers [23,24], application of conductive matter [25,26] and optimization of heating chamber structure [27,28]; (2) to improve the uniformity of microwave energy absorption, such as introducing of a rotating turntable or conveyor belt [29,30], optimization of the shapes and sizes of processing materials [26,31,32]. For studies on the electric discharge phenomena, related research has focused on microwave discharges in sintering of powdered metals. Attention is mainly paid to factors that influence the intensity and frequency of microwave discharges, such as the magnetron output power [14,33], the size, amount, conductivity, morphology and surface conditions of the metal [14,33–35] and the dielectric properties of the surrounding medium [15,35–37]. The lack of comprehensive consideration of the heating uniformity and safety of microwave heating solid stack materials has hindered the further application of microwave heating.

In this paper, a method to improve the heating uniformity and safety of microwave heating solid stack materials by introducing fluid materials with different dielectric properties is proposed. In Section two, a general model is built and computed with coupled physics of electromagnetic and heat transfer in solid and liquid. Based on simulation conditions, corresponding physical experiments are designed to complete the validation work. In Section three, comparisons between experimental results and computational ones are performed. Following the analysis of the influence of fluid materials' complex relative permittivity on the heating process, solutions to uniformity and unsafety issues are discussed.

2. Methodology

2.1. Multiphysics Simulation

2.1.1. Geometry

To build the general model for analyzing, the simulation model should be characterized with a simple structure and be intuitive to show the difference of heating results. Hence, a standard BJ22 waveguide with one end shortened is used as the heating cavity. The processing materials, silicon carbide spheres, and the fluid materials are placed in the cavity in a quartz cup. The model structure is built in a multi-physics software, COMSOL Multiphysics (5.3, COMSOL Inc., Stockholm, Sweden), which is shown in Figure 1.

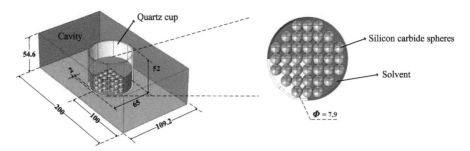

Figure 1. Geometry of the 3-D simulation model (unit: mm).

2.1.2. Governing Equations

The whole simulation is coupled of two physical processes: The microwave propagation process and heat transfer in solid and liquid process.

For the microwave propagation process, Maxwell's equations are used to solve the distribution of the electric field. The governing equations here are given as:

$$\begin{aligned}
\nabla \times \vec{H} &= \vec{J} + \varepsilon \frac{\partial \vec{E}}{\partial t} \\
\nabla \times \vec{E} &= -\frac{\partial \vec{B}}{\partial t} \\
\nabla \cdot \vec{B} &= 0 \\
\nabla \cdot \vec{D} &= \rho_e
\end{aligned} \tag{1}$$

where $\vec{H}$ is the magnetic field intensity, $\vec{J}$ is the ampere density, $\vec{E}$ is the electric field intensity, t is the time, $\vec{B}$ is the magnetic induction intensity, $\vec{D}$ is the electric displacement vector and ρ_e is the electric charge density. Equation (1) in the time harmonic field can be then written as the Helmholtz equation [38]

$$\nabla \times \mu_r^{-1}\left(\nabla \times \vec{E}\right) - k_0^2\left(\varepsilon_r\varepsilon_0 - \frac{j\sigma}{\omega}\right)\vec{E} = 0 \tag{2}$$

$$k_0 = \omega\sqrt{\varepsilon_0\mu_0}$$

where μ_r is the relative permeability, k_0 is the wave number in free space, ε_r is the relative permittivity, ε_0 is the permittivity of vacuum, ω is the angular frequency, σ is the electrical conductivity and μ_0 is the permeability of vacuum.

Then, the electromagnetic power loss Q_e of the processing materials can be gained from the computed electric field by the following equation [39,40]

$$Q_e = \frac{1}{2}\omega\varepsilon_0\varepsilon' \tan\delta\left|\vec{E}\right|^2 = \frac{1}{2}\omega\varepsilon_0\varepsilon''\left|\vec{E}\right|^2 \tag{3}$$

where ε' is the real part of the relative permittivity, ε'' is the imaginary part of the relative permittivity and $\tan\delta$ is the loss tangent of the processing materials.

For the heat transfer process, only the processing materials are involved to reduce the computation cost. The governing equation for heat transfer in solid and fluid is given as [41–43]

$$\rho C_p\frac{\partial T}{\partial t} - k\nabla^2 T = Q = Q_e \tag{4}$$

where ρ is the material density, C_p is the material heat capacity under atmospheric pressure, T is the temperature, Q is the heat source and k is the thermal conductivity.

2.1.3. Input Parameters and Boundary Conditions

To complete the simulation, necessary property parameters and boundary conditions are needed. Related input parameters are shown in Table 1. The thermal and dielectric properties of the processing materials are obtained from related literature [44–47] and modified by comparisons between experimental results and simulation results. The loss tangent of water (deionized), glycerol (analytical reagent, Yangzhou Feiyang chemical industry Co., Ltd, Yangzhou, China) and silicon carbide (99% purity, Hai Ning Zhijie pottery bearing Co., Ltd, Haining, China) is compared through the references [44–46] and the experiments at different temperatures, and the optimized data is chosen. It should be noted that the conductivity of silicon carbide is included by the loss tangent. The complex relative permittivity is defined as the processing materials to give a near-actual model, which is expressed as [48].

$$\varepsilon_r = \varepsilon' - \varepsilon'' = \varepsilon'(1 - j\tan\delta) \tag{5}$$

Table 1. Summary of material properties applied in the model.

	ε'	$\tan\delta$	μ_r	σ (S/m)	k (W/m·K)	ρ (kg/m³)	C_p (J/kg·K)
Air	1	0	1	0	2.524×10^{-2}	1.205	1005
Silicon carbide	12.3	0.12	1	0	450	3200	1600
Quartz	4.2	0	1	1×10^{-14}	10	2600	260
Water	79.4	0.12	1	5.5×10^{-6}	0.59	1000	4187
Glycerol	6.33	0.18	1	6.4×10^{-8}	0.27	1264	2735

For the microwave propagation process, one surface of the cavity is selected as the port where it feeds the electromagnetic energy at 2450 MHz in TE10 mode. Other surfaces are all defined as a perfect electric conductor, which can be expressed as the equation:

$$\vec{n} \times \vec{E} = 0 \tag{6}$$

where $\vec{n}$ is the unit normal vector of the corresponding surface.

For the heat transfer process, as only the processing materials are involved, all boundaries of the processing materials are defined as the thermal insulation boundary condition. The governing equation is given as

$$-\vec{n} \cdot \vec{q} = 0 \tag{7}$$

where $\vec{q}$ is the heat flux.

2.1.4. Mesh Size

Appropriate mesh size in the model simulation can provide accurate simulation results with higher computation efficiency. The space discretization errors could be down to a quarter when mesh size is halved, while the computation time will increase by almost 16 times [49].

To determine the appropriate mesh size in our model, normalized power absorption (NPA) of the processing materials has been employed to complete the mesh independent study [37]. Here, the variation of NPA with mesh sizes is shown in Figure 2. The manual of software QuickWave (QWED, Warsaw, Poland) suggests there to be 12 cells per wavelength for mesh independent results while other researchers [50] suggest 10 cells per wavelength is enough. The mesh size used in this paper is defined as

$$m_{meshsize} \leq \frac{c}{6f\sqrt{\varepsilon_r}} \tag{8}$$

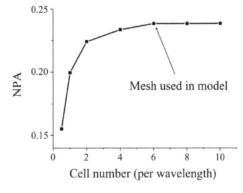

Figure 2. Normalized power absorption (NPA) variation of heating computations with different mesh sizes.

2.1.5. Simulation Process

In the simulation, the electromagnetic field distribution is firstly calculated in the frequency domain, and then the dissipated power is calculated. Finally, the temperature rise of the material is updated through the heat transfer equation in the time domain. Since the electrical properties of samples do not vary with temperature, the electromagnetic field distribution will not change and is only calculated once. The whole heating process lasts 120 s, and the computation time of the model depends on the mesh size and the memory of the computer. In this simulation, the mesh sizes of the model with water and model with glycerol are 808,998 and 455,672, respectively. The computation time of each model is 7317 s and 3354 s in a computer with a memory of 128 GB.

2.2. Experimental Setup

2.2.1. Experiment System

To validate the computation results, physical experiments need to be completed. The whole experimental system is shown in Figures 3 and 4. Microwave power is generated from a microwave generator (WSPS-2450-1000M, Wattsine, Chengdu, China) to a waveguide coaxial connector (CAWG-26-N, Euler, Nanjing, China). A circulator connected with water load is employed to protect the source from the reflection power. With a dual directional coupler and a power meter (AV2433, the 41st Institute of CETC, Tsingtao, China) as power monitoring, microwave power is finally fed into the BJ22 waveguide connected with a slide short. Final heating temperature is gained by a fiber optic thermometer (FISO FOT-NS-967A, FISO Technologies, Quebec, QC, Canada).

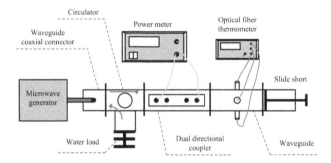

Figure 3. Schematic of the laboratory microwave heating system.

Figure 4. The laboratory microwave heating system.

2.2.2. Experimental Procedures

Physical experiments are carried out with 55 W microwave power at 2.45 GHz. For temperature measurements, several fibers of the fiber optic thermometer have been used and connected to the processing materials through the cut-off waveguide on the BJ22 waveguide. For power measurements, a power meter is employed to verify the incidence and reflection situation of the microwave power. To give more evident temperature rise and make the experiment easier, the length between the quartz cup and the slide short is set as λ_e, which is defined as

$$\lambda_e = \frac{3}{2} \cdot \frac{\lambda}{\sqrt{1 - \left(\frac{f_c}{f}\right)^2}}, \lambda = c/f \tag{9}$$

where λ is the wavelength of the microwave in vacuum, f_c is the cut-off frequency of the BJ22 waveguide, f is the frequency of the microwave. The corresponding modification of the experimental length of the BJ22 waveguide is realized by the slide short. A simple test system, shown in Figure 5, is performed to adjust the position of the slide short. By combining the S_{11} gained from the vector network analyzer (N5230A, Agilent Technologies Inc., Santa Clara, CA, USA), the position of the slide short is confirmed to match the simulation.

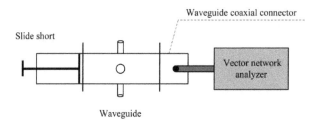

Figure 5. Schematic of the simple system for the slide short position confirmation.

3. Results and Discussion

3.1. Experiment Validation

To validate the simulation results, one experiment group with water as the polar solvent while another with glycerol as the non-polar solvent is employed. In the experiments, the silicon carbide spheres are actually placed in a two-layer structure as shown in Figure 6. The same adjustment has been done to the corresponding simulation model.

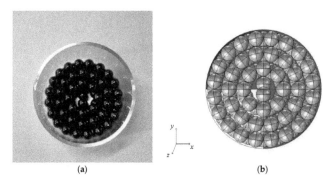

(a)   (b)

Figure 6. Structure of the silicon carbide spheres: (a) Experimental structure; (b) simulation structure.

Two points of the processing materials have been chosen to perform the temperature variation comparisons between the experiment and the simulation (shown in Figure 7). The center bottom of the quartz cup is selected as the origin of the axes and directions of the axes are shown in Figure 6b. Comparisons show that simulation results match the experiential results well.

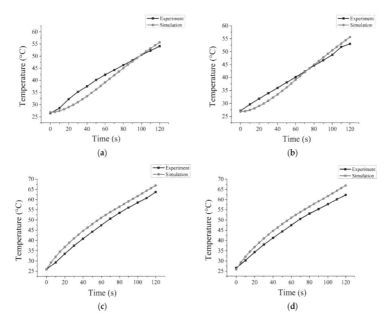

Figure 7. Temperature variation comparisons between the experiment and simulation: (**a**) Temperature of point (5,0,0) with water as the fluid material; (**b**) temperature of point (−5,0,0) with water as the fluid material; (**c**) temperature of point (5,0,0) with glycerol as the fluid material; (**d**) temperature of point (−5,0,0) with glycerol as the fluid material.

3.2. Effect of Introducing Fluid Materials with Different Dielectric Properties

To give intuitive and convictive results of the influence of the fluid materials on the heating uniformity and safety, a more compact three-layer structure is applied to the simulated silicon carbide spheres and the computations are divided into two situations, where only ε' of fluid materials is computed and where both ε' and ε'' are taken into consideration, respectively. Since properties of other related materials stay the same, the other physical properties of the fluid materials have all been defined to be the same with water to avoid their distractions. Meanwhile, the microwave power is set as 100 W and the density of water is set as 1 kg/m^3 in order to get a higher temperature rise, and the initial temperature is set as 20 degrees centigrade. The whole heating process lasts 120 s. In the computation results, the reflection parameters S_{11} of the heating system, the average body temperature $\overline{T}$ of the solids, the coefficient of variation (COV) value of the solids' final temperature and the maximum modulus value of the electric field $|\overrightarrow{E}|_{max}$ in the whole processing materials are analyzed. The COV of temperature can be expressed by

$$COV = \frac{\sqrt{\frac{1}{N}\sum_{i=1}^{N}(T_i - \overline{T})^2}}{\overline{T} - T_0} \qquad (10)$$

where N is the total number of the temperature points, T_i is the temperature at a point, $\overline{T}$ is the average temperature and T_0 is the initial temperature. Generally speaking, the smaller the COV of the temperature, the smaller the dispersion degree of the temperature distribution, which means the better heating uniformity.

For the first situation, S_{11}, $\overline{T}$, COV and $|\overrightarrow{E}|_{max}$ along with ε' are shown in Figure 8. It is worthy to note that the reflection parameter is calculated by the rate of reflection power and incident power. Computation results of the system are firstly characterized by the reflection coefficient S_{11}, namely the power absorbed by the processing materials. As shown in Figure 8a, the increasing of ε' has obvious but nonlinear effects on the S_{11} and will thus decide the corresponding $\overline{T}$ through its impact on the microwave feeding condition.

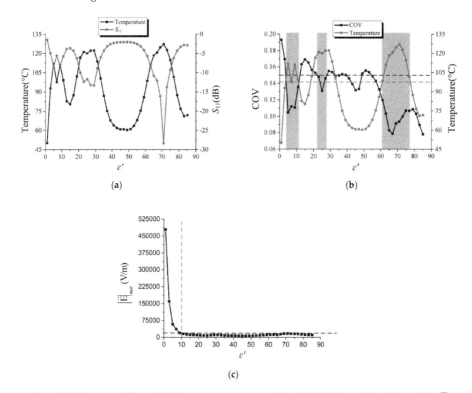

(a)

(b)

(c)

Figure 8. Influence of ε' on the final parameters at time 120 s: (a) Variations of the S_{11} and the $\overline{T}$; (b) variations of the coefficient of variation (COV) and $\overline{T}$; (c) variations of the $|\overrightarrow{E}|_{max}$.

To the heating uniformity of the processing solids, the COV variation shows that it will mainly decrease with the rise of ε', e.g., it decreases from 0.1931 with $\varepsilon' = 1$ to 0.0782 with $\varepsilon' = 85$. However, in small ranges, it should be analyzed more precisely as the COV has fluctuated. Combined with the analyzed $\overline{T}$ condition, areas where uniform heating with high efficiency could be gained just like the marked areas in Figure 8b.

For the heating safety of the processing materials, the increase of ε' in a certain region (from ε' = 1 to $\varepsilon' = 10$ as marked in Figure 8c) has a remarkable effect on lowering the $|\overrightarrow{E}|_{max}$ as it changes from 478,870 V/m to 19,982 V/m, which is reduced by about 24 times. Out of this range, the influence of the increasing ε' stays weak. The differences could be further described by the mean square error as it is 191,152.0 V/m in the former range while it is 3109.9 V/m in the latter, which is reduced by about 60.5 times. Compared with normal heating solids with air surroundings, namely $\varepsilon' = 1$, the introduction of fluid materials with proper ε' shows a more convenient way to achieve uniform and safe microwave heating.

After computations of ε' only, the influences of ε'' have also been studied. The related computation results shown in Table 2 and Figure 9, and the increasing of ε'' from 0 to 0.3 will lower the S_{11} and thus bring more efficient heating. While the S_{11} and $\overline{T}$ almost stay the same out of this range.

To the heating uniformity and safety, introducing fluid materials with higher ε'' could reduce the $|\overrightarrow{E}|_{max}$, as the increasing of ε'' from 0.1 to 0.9 has reduced the $|\overrightarrow{E}|_{max}$ by about 34% to 55%. However, higher ε'' will cause worse heating uniformity as shown in Figure 9b.

Table 2. Comparisons of the COV and $|\overrightarrow{E}|_{max}$ while ε'' is considered.

ε'	$\tan\delta$	$S_{11}(\text{dB})$	$\overline{T}(°C)$	COV	$|\overrightarrow{E}|_{max}(\text{V/m})$
	0	−3.5994	80.48	0.160856772	12,105
15	0.1	−5.0345	93.66	0.145737029	10,183
	0.5	−7.3592	107.61	0.202485855	4558.9
	0.9	−7.6533	108.9	0.229677999	4136.1
	0	−2.0435	60.28	0.154154613	7525.2
50	0.1	−3.8066	82.65	0.122400265	6047.8
	0.5	−5.9392	99.98	0.170629879	4484.6
	0.9	−5.8709	99.54	0.193053244	4136.1
	0	−2.8677	71.88	0.073144433	10,796
85	0.1	−4.0862	85.44	0.088155288	8663.5
	0.5	−5.0389	93.68	0.176975505	6465.7
	0.9	−4.9559	93.03	0.198345404	5898

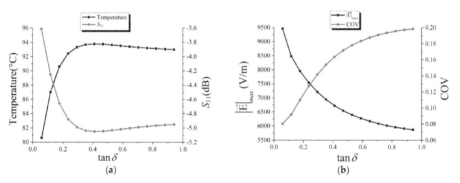

Figure 9. Influence of ε'' on the final parameters with $\varepsilon' = 85$ at time 120 s: (**a**) Variations of the S_{11} and the $\overline{T}$; (**b**) variations of the COV and the $|\overrightarrow{E}|_{max}$.

As the computation results analyzed above, the introduction of fluid materials with proper relative permittivity does improve the heating uniformity and safety of microwave heating of common stack solid materials. For the real part of relative permittivity of fluid materials, the computed $|\overrightarrow{E}|_{max}$ in simulation models is always gained in the interface between the solids and the fluid materials. Combined with the cure trend shown Figure 8b and the relative permittivity of the solids shown in Table 1, it is deduced that the maximum modulus value of the electric field $|\overrightarrow{E}|_{max}$ stays huge when the ε' of fluid materials is much different with the one of solids. A comparison of the variation of

$\mid \overrightarrow{E} \mid_{max}$ on fluid materials' ε' with solids of different relative permittivity is performed in Figure 10 and the simulation results have agreed with our deduction.

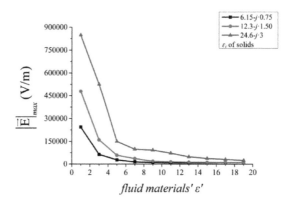

Figure 10. The influence of ε' on the $\mid \overrightarrow{E} \mid_{max}$.

When dealing with certain solids, introducing fluid materials with higher ε' can efficiently lower the maximum modulus value of the electric field in order to make a safer heating process. The higher ε' is also good for improving heating uniformity. On the other hand, the increasing of ε'' in a certain range could obviously improve the heating efficiency and in the whole range its increase will lower the maximum modulus value of the electric field, but bring worse heating uniformity. Since the involved factors are complicated, a proper choice of ε'' to balance the requirements between heating uniformity and safety should be made in the practical situation.

4. Conclusions

In this work, a general model has been built to study the influence of introducing fluid materials in the heating uniformity and safety of microwave heating solid stack materials. Simulations are computed by COMSOL Multiphysics based on the finite element method. With the mesh independence study and adjustment corresponding to physical experiments, the model has been verified and its simulation results agree well with validation experiments.

The real part of relative permittivity of the introduced fluid materials could significantly lower the maximum modulus value of the electric field in a range of $\varepsilon' = 1$ to $\varepsilon' = 10$, but out of this range its influence stays low. The increase of ε' on the whole studied range will improve the heating uniformity, but in small ranges it has fluctuated. The increase of the imaginary part of relative permittivity from 0 to 0.3 could obviously improve the heating efficiency. On the whole studied range, higher ε'' could lower the maximum modulus value of the electric field and give a safer heating, but it will make the heating uniformity worse. Combined with computational results, the general rules of the influence of fluid materials' relative permittivity on the heating uniformity and safety may be useful for the practical heating process.

Author Contributions: T.H. and H.Z. conceived and designed the experiments; J.W. performed the experiments; J.W. and Y.H. developed the model, analyzed the data and wrote the initial draft of the manuscript; T.X. and F.Y. assisted the experiment procedures; T.H. reviewed and contributed to the final manuscript.

Funding: This work was funded by Sichuan Science and Technology Program (Grant No. 2018FZ0008), Guizhou Science and Technology Program (Grant No. Qiankehezhicheng [2018]2004) and State Key Laboratory of Efficient Utilization for Low Grade Phosphate Rock and Its Associated Resources (Grant No. WFKF2017-05).

Conflicts of Interest: The authors declare no conflict of interest.

References

1. Demirskyi, D.; Agrawal, D.; Ragulya, A. Neck formation between copper spherical particles under single-mode and multimode microwave sintering. *Mater. Sci. Eng. A* **2010**, *527*, 2142–2145. [CrossRef]

2. Ozkoc, S.O.; Sumnu, G.; Sahin, S. Recent Developments in Microwave Heating. In *Emerging Technologies for Food Processing*, 2nd ed.; Elsevier Ltd.: Amsterdam, The Netherlands, 2015; Chapter 20; pp. 361–383.

3. Ferrera-Lorenzo, N.; Fuente, E.; Suárez-Ruiz, I.; Ruiz, B. KOH activated carbon from conventional and microwave heating system of a macroalgae waste from the Agar–Agar industry. *Fuel Process. Technol.* **2014**, *121*, 25–31. [CrossRef]

4. Monteiro, R.L.; Carciofi, B.A.M.; Marsaioli, A., Jr.; Laurindo, J.B. How to make a microwave vacuum dryer with turntable. *J. Food Eng.* **2015**, *166*, 276–284. [CrossRef]

5. Wu, Y.; Hong, T.; Tang, Z.; Zhang, C. Dynamic Model for a Uniform Microwave-Assisted Continuous Flow Process of Ethyl Acetate Production. *Entropy* **2018**, *20*, 241. [CrossRef]

6. Adam, D. Microwave chemistry: Out of the kitchen. *Nature* **2003**, *421*, 571–572. [CrossRef] [PubMed]

7. Vadivambal, R.; Jayas, D.S. Non-uniform temperature distribution during microwave heating of food materials—A review. *Food Bioprocess Technol.* **2010**, *3*, 161–171. [CrossRef]

8. Kubota, M.; Hanada, T.; Yabe, S.; Kuchar, D.; Matsuda, H. Water desorption behavior of desiccant rotor under microwave irradiation. *Appl. Therm. Eng.* **2011**, *31*, 1482–1486. [CrossRef]

9. Lopez-Avila, V.; Benedicto, J.; Bauer, K.M. Stability of organochlorine and organophosphorus pesticides when extracted from solid matrixes with microwave energy. *J. AOAC Int.* **1998**, *81*, 1224–1232.

10. Sebera, V.; Nasswettrová, A.; Nikl, K. Finite element analysis of mode stirrer impact on electric field uniformity in a microwave applicator. *Dry. Technol.* **2012**, *30*, 1388–1396. [CrossRef]

11. Hong, T.; Tang, Z.; Zhu, H. Anomalous dielectric relaxation with linear reaction dynamics in space-dependent force fields. *J. Chem. Phys.* **2016**, *145*, 244105. [CrossRef] [PubMed]

12. Stadler, A.; Yousefi, B.H.; Dallinger, D.; Walla, P.; Van der Eycken, E.; Kaval, N.; Kappe, C.O. Scalability of microwave-assisted organic synthesis. From single-mode to multimode parallel batch reactors. *Org. Process Res. Dev.* **2003**, *7*, 707–716. [CrossRef]

13. Wu, X. Experimental and Theoretical Study of Microwave Heating of Thermal Runaway Materials. Ph.D. Thesis, Virginia Tech, Virginia Polytechnic Institute and State University, Blacksburg, VA, USA, 18 December 2002.

14. Wang, W.; Liu, Z.; Sun, J.; Ma, Q.; Ma, C.; Zhang, Y. Experimental study on the heating effects of microwave discharge caused by metals. *AIChE J.* **2012**, *58*, 3852–3857. [CrossRef]

15. Sun, J.; Wang, W.; Zhao, C.; Zhang, Y.; Ma, C.; Yue, Q. Study on the coupled effect of wave absorption and metal discharge generation under microwave irradiation. *Ind. Eng. Chem. Res.* **2014**, *53*, 2042–2051. [CrossRef]

16. Sun, J.; Wang, W.; Liu, Z.; Ma, C. Recycling of waste printed circuit boards by microwave-induced pyrolysis and featured mechanical processing. *Ind. Eng. Chem. Res.* **2011**, *50*, 11763–11769. [CrossRef]

17. Sun, J.; Wang, W.; Liu, Z.; Ma, Q.; Zhao, C.; Ma, C. Kinetic study of the pyrolysis of waste printed circuit boards subject to conventional and microwave heating. *Energies* **2012**, *5*, 3295–3306. [CrossRef]

18. Li, Z.Y.; Wang, R.F.; Kudra, T. Uniformity issue in microwave drying. *Dry. Technol.* **2011**, *29*, 652–660. [CrossRef]

19. Campañone, L.A.; Bava, J.A.; Mascheroni, R.H. Modeling and process simulation of controlled microwave heating of foods by using of the resonance phenomenon. *Appl. Therm. Eng.* **2014**, *73*, 914–923. [CrossRef]

20. Luan, D.; Tang, J.; Pedrow, P.D.; Liu, F.; Tang, Z. Analysis of electric field distribution within a microwave assisted thermal sterilization (MATS) system by computer simulation. *J. Food Eng.* **2016**, *188*, 87–97. [CrossRef]

21. Lin, B.Q.; Li, H.; Dai, H.M.; Zhu, C.J.; Yao, H. Three-dimensional simulation of microwave heating coal sample with varying parameters. *Appl. Therm. Eng.* **2016**, *93*, 1145–1154.

22. Bae, S.H.; Jeong, M.G.; Kim, J.H.; Lee, W.S. A continuous power-controlled microwave belt drier improving heating uniformity. *IEEE Microw. Wirel. Compon. Lett.* **2017**, *27*, 527–529. [CrossRef]

23. Plaza-González, P.; Monzó-Cabrera, J.; Catalá-Civera, J.M.; Sánchez-Hernández, D. New approach for the prediction of the electric field distribution in multimode microwave-heating applicators with mode stirrers. *IEEE Trans. Magn.* **2004**, *40*, 1672–1678. [CrossRef]

24. Plaza-González, P.; Monzó-Cabrera, J.; Catalá-Civera, J.M.; Sánchez-Hernández, D. Effect of mode-stirrer configurations on dielectric heating performance in multimode microwave applicators. *IEEE Trans. Microw. Theory Tech.* **2005**, *53*, 1699–1706. [CrossRef]
25. Wang, R.; Huo, H.; Dou, R.; Li, Z.; Mujumdar, A.S. Effect of the inside placement of electrically conductive beads on electric field uniformity in a microwave applicator. *Dry. Technol.* **2014**, *32*, 1997–2004. [CrossRef]
26. Meng, Q.; Lan, J.; Hong, T.; Zhu, H. Effect of the rotating metal patch on microwave heating uniformity. *J. Microw. Power Electromagn. Energy* **2018**, *52*, 94–108. [CrossRef]
27. Zhou, R.; Yang, X.; Sun, D.; Jia, G. Multiple tube structure for heating uniformity and efficiency optimization of microwave ovens. *Eur. Phys. J. Appl. Phys.* **2015**, *69*, 20201. [CrossRef]
28. Raaholt, B.W.; Isaksson, S.; Hamberg, L.; Fhager, A.; Hamnerius, Y. Continuous tubular microwave heating of homogeneous foods: evaluation of heating uniformity. *J. Microw. Power Electromagn. Energy* **2016**, *50*, 43–65. [CrossRef]
29. Ryynänen, S.; Ohlsson, T. Microwave heating uniformity of ready meals as affected by placement, composition, and geometry. *J. Food Sci.* **1996**, *61*, 620–624. [CrossRef]
30. Geedipalli, S.S.R.; Rakesh, V.; Datta, A.K. Modeling the heating uniformity contributed by a rotating turntable in microwave ovens. *J. Food Eng.* **2007**, *82*, 359–368. [CrossRef]
31. Salema, A.A.; Afzal, M.T. Numerical simulation of heating behaviour in biomass bed and pellets under multimode microwave system. *Int. J. Therm. Sci.* **2015**, *91*, 12–24. [CrossRef]
32. Soto-Reyes, N.; Temis-Pérez, A.L.; López-Malo, A.; Rojas-Laguna, R.; Sosa-Morales, M.E. Effects of shape and size of agar gels on heating uniformity during pulsed microwave treatment. *J. Food Sci.* **2015**, *80*, E1021–E1025. [CrossRef] [PubMed]
33. Chen, W.; Gutmann, B.; Kappe, C.O. Characterization of Microwave-Induced Electric Discharge Phenomena in Metal–Solvent Mixtures. *ChemistryOpen* **2012**, *1*, 39–48. [CrossRef] [PubMed]
34. Hu, C.; Xi, X.; Huang, Z.; Zhan, Z. Simple Analysis of Mechanism of Microware Sintering of Metal Powder. *Mater. Rev.* **2008**, *S2*, 329–332. (In Chinese)
35. Whittaker, A.G.; Mingos, D.M.P. Arcing and other microwave characteristics of metal powders in liquid systems. *J. Chem. Soc. Dalton Trans.* **2000**, *9*, 1521–1526. [CrossRef]
36. Lide, D.R. *CRC Handbook of Chemistry and Physic*, 90th ed.; CRC Press: Boca Raton, FL, USA, 2012; pp. 15–46.
37. Perreux, L.; Loupy, A.; Petit, A. Nonthermal effects of microwaves in organic synthesis. In *Microwaves in Organic Synthesis*, 3rd ed.; De la Hoz, A., Loupy, A., Eds.; Wiley—VCH Verlag GmbH & Co. KGaA: Weinheim, Germany, 2012; Chapter 4, pp. 127–207.
38. Torres, F.; Jecko, B. Complete FDTD analysis of microwave heating processes in frequency-dependent and temperature-dependent media. *IEEE Trans. Microw. Theory* **1997**, *45*, 108–117. [CrossRef]
39. Goldblith, S.A.; Wang, D.I. Effect of microwaves on Escherichia coli and Bacillus subtilis. *Appl. Microbiol.* **1967**, *15*, 1371–1375. [PubMed]
40. Huang, K.M.; Liao, Y.H. Transient power loss density of electromagnetic pulse in debye media. *IEEE Trans. Microw. Theory* **2015**, *63*, 135–140. [CrossRef]
41. Pandit, R.B.; Prasad, S. Finite element analysis of microwave heating of potato—Transient temperature profiles. *J. Food Eng.* **2003**, *60*, 193–202. [CrossRef]
42. Pitchai, K.; Birla, S.L.; Subbiah, J.; Jones, D.; Thippareddi, H. Coupled electromagnetic and heat transfer model for microwave heating in domestic ovens. *J. Food Eng.* **2012**, *112*, 100–111. [CrossRef]
43. Pitchai, K.; Chen, J.; Birla, S.; Gonzalez, R.; Jones, D.; Subbiah, J. A microwave heat transfer model for a rotating multi-component meal in a domestic oven: development and validation. *J. Food Eng.* **2014**, *128*, 60–71. [CrossRef]
44. Zhu, H.; Ye, J.; Gulati, T.; Yang, Y.; Liao, Y.; Yang, Y.; Huang, K. Dynamic analysis of continuous-flow microwave reactor with a screw propeller. *Appl. Therm. Eng.* **2017**, *123*, 1456–1461. [CrossRef]
45. Grant, E.; Halstead, B.J. Dielectric parameters relevant to microwave dielectric heating. *Chem. Soc. Rev.* **1998**, *27*, 213–224.
46. Kuang, J.; Cao, W. Silicon carbide whiskers: Preparation and high dielectric permittivity. *J. Am. Ceram. Soc.* **2013**, *96*, 2877–2880. [CrossRef]
47. Ye, J.; Hong, T.; Wu, Y.; Wu, L.; Liao, Y.; Zhu, H.; Yang, Y.; Huang, K. Model stirrer based on a multi-material turntable for microwave processing materials. *Materials* **2017**, *10*, 95. [CrossRef] [PubMed]

48. Böttcher, C.J.F.; van Belle, O.C.; Bordewijk, P.; Rip, A.; Yue, D.D. Theory of electric polarization. *J. Electrochem. Soc.* **1974**, *121*, 211C. [CrossRef]
49. QuickWave EM simulator, QWED s.c., Zwyciezcow 34/2, 03-938 Warsaw, Poland. Available online: http: //www.qwed.com.pl/ (accessed on 6 November 2018).
50. Pathak, S.K.; Liu, F.; Tang, J. Finite difference time domain (FDTD) characterization of a single mode applicator. *J. Microw. Power Electromagn. Energy* **2003**, *38*, 37–48. [CrossRef]

Article

Simulation and Analysis of Oleic Acid Pretreatment for Microwave-Assisted Biodiesel Production

Weiquan Ma [1], Tao Hong [2], Tian Xie [3], Fengxia Wang [3], Bin Luo [1], Jie Zhou [1], Yang Yang [1], Huacheng Zhu [1,*] and Kama Huang [1]

[1]   College of Electronic and Information Engineering, Sichuan University, Chengdu 610065, China; maweiquan17@163.com (W.M.); luobin142@163.com (B.L.); Zhoujie_cc@163.com (J.Z.); yyang@scu.edu.cn (Y.Y.); kmhuang126@126.com (K.H.)

[2]   School of Electronic Information Engineering, China West Normal University, Nanchong 637002, China; cwnu_thong@163.com

[3]   State Key Laboratory of Efficient Utilization for Low Grade Phosphate Rock and Its Associated Resources, Wengfu Group, Guiyang 550014, China; xietian@wengfu.com (T.X.); wangfengxia9999@163.com (F.W.)

*   Correspondence: hczhu@scu.edu.cn; Fax: +86-28-8547-0659

Received: 12 June 2018; Accepted: 24 August 2018; Published: 28 August 2018

Abstract: Oleic acid needs to be heated when it is utilized for biodiesel production, but, as a low-loss solution, oleic acid is difficult to heat by microwave. An efficient heating method for oleic acid is designed. A high loss material porous media is placed in a quartz tube, and a microwave directly heats the porous medium of the high loss material. The oleic acid flows through the pores of porous media so that the oleic acid exchanges heat during this process and rapid heating of oleic acid is achieved. A coupling model, based on the finite element method, is used to analyze the microwave heating process. The multiphysics model is based on a single mode cavity operating at 2450 MHz. An elaborate experimental system is developed to validate the multiphysics model through temperature measurements carried out for different flow velocities of oleic acid and different microwave power levels. The computational results are in good agreement with the experimental data. Based on the validated model, the effects of different sizes, porosities, and materials on microwave heating efficiency are analyzed.

Keywords: microwave heating; biodiesel; oleic acid; coupling; multiphysics calculation

---

1. Introduction

As an environmentally-friendly fuel, biodiesel offers the advantages of low toxicity, low CO_2 emissions, high safety, excellent combustion performance, and good reproducibility compared with traditional petroleum diesel. The main components of biodiesel are long-chain saturated and unsaturated fatty acids, such as palmitic acid, stearic acid, oleic acid, linoleic acid, and ester compounds formed from short chain alcohols, such as methanol or ethanol [1–6]. Oleic acid needs to be heated to esterify. The temperature required for oleic acid in microwave-assisted biodiesel production is 60 °C. Higher reaction temperatures, longer reaction times, and larger amounts of catalyst are often requisite during the esterinterchange reaction. As a new heating method, microwave can greatly improve the reaction rate. Compared with the traditional heating method, microwave possesses numerous advantages, such as improved quality and instantaneous control [7,8]. Due to its unique heating principle, microwave heating has been widely used in various fields. However, its industrial implementation has been less broadly embraced, and it is limited primarily to applications in materials drying and food processing.

Microwave heating depends on the dielectric properties of materials [9,10]. The effects of microwave heating are useful when the microwave acts on polar molecules directly. When the polar molecular medium is placed in the microwave field, the existing molecules will be rotating along with the high-frequency electric field. As the field alternates, the molecules reverse direction. Rotating molecules push, pull, and collide with other molecules (through electrical forces), distributing the energy to adjacent molecules and atoms in the material. The process of energy transfer from the microwave to the sample is a form of radiative heating. In this microscopic process, the more microwave energy that enters the medium, the higher is the temperature of the medium.

Although oleic acid contains a carboxyl group as a carboxylic acid, its dielectric loss is very low. When the temperature is 27 °C and the frequency is 2450 MHz, the imaginary part of complex permittivity is approximately 0.0074, which means that oleic acid is difficult to be directly heated by a microwave.

In this paper, a model has been designed to overcome the problem in which oleic acid cannot be heated by microwave. A porous silicon carbide was employed to absorb the microwave energy and to transfer this energy to oleic acid. Moreover, a multiphysics model, including electromagnetism, fluid heat transfer, and free and porous media flow was built. The temperature increase at different powers and flow velocities was calculated. The model describes a single-mode cavity operating at a frequency of 2450 MHz with a relatively uniform and unidirectional electric field. Next, an elaborate experimental system was developed to validate the multiphysics model through temperature measurements performed for different solution velocities of oleic acid and different microwave powers, and temperature was measured at three points of the outlet for different solution velocities to verify heating uniformity. Finally, the effects of tube size and material porosity on microwave heating efficiency were analyzed. The optimization of the model was completed, and a high efficiency microwave heating system design was achieved.

2. Methodology

2.1. Multiphysics Simulation

2.1.1. Geometry

A 3D geometry of the experimental system above was built in commercial finite element software, COMSOL Multiphysics 5.2a (COMSOL Inc., Newton, MA, USA). A 2D cross-section of the geometry is shown in Figure 1. A WR430 (109.2 mm × 54.6 mm) waveguide was used in the geometry, as presented in Figure 1. The waveguide is used to orient the electromagnetic wave. The frequency of the electromagnetic wave transmitted in the WR430 waveguide is from 1.72 GHz to 2.61 GHz. In addition, the dimension of the geometry in the direction perpendicular to the 2D cross section is 109.2 mm. A glass tube was employed to carry the fluid. The height of silicon carbide is 54.6 mm, which is the same as BJ22 waveguide's height. Four faces of the waveguide were set as a Perfect Electric Conductor. The left side of the waveguide was excitation.

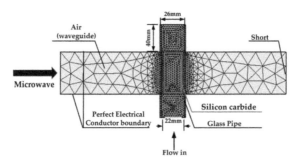

Figure 1. The geometry of the microwave heating.

The oleic acid flows through the pores inside of the porous medium and is heated in the form of heat conduction inside of the porous medium. The glass tube has been assumed as a non-loss material. Its dielectric loss factor is zero, and it has a dielectric constant value of 4.2. The porous medium is heated faster by microwave heating, and oleic acid flows through the pores inside of the porous medium to achieve the purpose of rapid heating of oleic acid.

2.1.2. Governing Equations

For the multiphysics calculation of microwave heating oleic acid model, the electromagnetic field, the heat in fluid, and the free and porous media flow modules are coupled with each other.

For the electromagnetic field, it is given by Maxwell's equations:

$$
\begin{aligned}
\nabla \times \vec{H} &= \vec{J} + \frac{\partial \vec{D}}{\partial t} \\
\nabla \times \vec{E} &= -\mu \frac{\partial \vec{H}}{\partial t} \\
\nabla \cdot \vec{B} &= 0 \\
\nabla \cdot \vec{D} &= \rho_e,
\end{aligned}
\tag{1}
$$

where $\vec{E}$ and $\vec{H}$ are the electric field and magnetic field intensity, respectively; $\vec{D}$ is the electric field flux intensity; $\vec{B}$ is the magnetic field flux intensity; $\vec{J}$ is the conduction current; μ is the permeability; and ρ_e is the free charge density.

The electromagnetic power loss Q_e could be obtained from the computed electric field by the following equation [11,12], where ε_0 is the permittivity of free space; and ε'' is the imaginary part of the relative permittivity of the materials.

$$
Q_e = \frac{1}{2}\omega\varepsilon_0\varepsilon''|\vec{E}|^2.
\tag{2}
$$

The temperature distribution of the porous media solid in this model can be computed by the governing equation for heat transfer in solids, as given as [13–15].

The temperature of the porous media could be obtained by the heat equation:

$$
\rho C_p \frac{\partial T}{\partial t} - k\nabla^2 T = Q = Q_e,
\tag{3}
$$

where ρ is the fluid density; C_P is the fluid heat capacity at constant pressure; T is the temperature; t is the time; Q is the heat source; and k is the thermal conductivity.

For the fluid modules, flow in the free channel is described by the Navier Stokes equations:

$$
\begin{aligned}
\nabla \cdot [\mu(\nabla\vec{u} \cdot \vec{I} + (\nabla\vec{u})^T) - p \cdot \vec{I}] &= \rho(\vec{u} \cdot \nabla)\vec{u}, \\
\rho\nabla \cdot \vec{u} &= 0,
\end{aligned}
\tag{4}
$$

where $\vec{u}$ refers to the velocity in the open channel (m/s), $\vec{I}$ is identity matrix, and p is the pressure (Pa).

In COMSOL Multiphysics, free flow and porous media flow are effortlessly combined using the Brinkman equations:

$$
\begin{aligned}
\frac{\rho}{\varepsilon_p}((\vec{u} \cdot \nabla)\frac{\vec{u}}{\varepsilon_p}) + \frac{\mu}{k}\vec{u} &= \nabla \cdot [-p \cdot \vec{I} + \frac{\mu}{\varepsilon_p}(\nabla\vec{u} + (\nabla\vec{u})^T) - \frac{2}{3}\mu(\nabla \cdot \vec{u})\vec{I}], \\
\rho\nabla \cdot \vec{u} &= 0,
\end{aligned}
\tag{5}
$$

where η denotes the dynamic viscosity (Pa s), k denotes the permeability of porous medium (m^2), ρ is the fluid's density (kg/m^3), the ε_p is the porosity (dimensionless).

The Darcy's law is used to calculate a relatively slow flow in a porous medium, where the shear stress effect perpendicular to the flow direction is very small. The Brinkman equations further considers the loss of mechanical energy by viscous shear forces based on Darcy's law. In addition, the Brinkman equations describe flow through certain porous media as a particular continuum model for a mixture of two materials, where one is modeled as a rigid solid, and the other as an incompressible fluid.

As can be seen from the Navier Stokes equations and Brinkman equations, the momentum transport equations are closely related. They are also utilized to calculate high velocity porous flow [16–19]. The equations and Brinkman equations can be coupled to calculate solution flow [20,21]. The different terms correspond to the inertial forces, pressure forces, viscous forces, and external forces that are applied to the fluid.

2.1.3. Input Parameters

The thermo-physical properties of the fluid (density, dynamic viscosity, specific heat, and thermal conductivity) were obtained from references, as shown in Table 1. The initial simulation temperature of oleic acid was measured by an experiment.

Table 1. Summary of material properties applied in the model.

Property	Relative Permittivity	Dynamic Viscosities (Pa·s)	Conductivity (S/m)	Heat Conductivity Coefficient (W/m·K)
Oleic acid	$2.563 - j \times 0.0074$	$0.00249 + 1663.122 \times \exp(-T/26.876)$ [22]	3×10^{-13}	$0.3292 - 0.000331 \times T$ [23]
Silicon carbide	$20.08 - j \times 1.5$ (in this study)	-	0.16 (in this study)	1280 (in this study)
Silicon nitride	$7.8 - j \times 0.05$ [24]	-	0.11 [25]	18.42 [26]
Air	1	-	0	2.524
Quartz	4.2	-	1×10^{-14}	10

Property	Heat Capacity at Constant Pressure (J/kg·K)	Factor of Porosity	Density (kg/m³)	Heat Capacity at Constant Pressure (J/kg·K)
Oleic acid	$2670.852 + 4.147 \times T$	0.9 (by measurement)	$1100.15 - 0.698 \times T$ [22]	$2670.852 + 4.147 \times T$
Silicon carbide	1600 (in this study)	-	580 (in this study)	1600 (in this study)
Silicon nitride	710 [26]	-	3198 [27]	710 [26]
Air	1005	-	1.205	1005
Quartz	260	-	2600	260

Relative permittivity constitutes a critical parameter for the calculation of the multiphysics field of microwave heating. This parameter is influenced by both frequency and temperature [28]. In this study, the complex permittivity of oleic acid was obtained by measurement, and the measurement system is shown in Figure 2. The measurement equipment was a vector network analyzer (N5245B, Agilent Technologies, Inc., Santa Clara, CA, USA) and high-performance test probe (N1501A, Agilent Technologies, Inc., Santa Clara, CA, USA). The measurement results are shown in Table 2. When the temperature is within 70 °C, the imaginary part of the oleic acid's complex permittivity is approximately 0.005. The value is close to zero, and the dipole moment is small. Consequently, the molecules of oleic acid are difficult to deflect in the electric field and thus cannot be directly heated by microwave. Moreover, because the thermal stability of silicon carbide is very good [29,30], its complex permittivity changes very little with temperature rising, so the dielectric constants of silicon carbide and oleic acid are calculated as constants here.

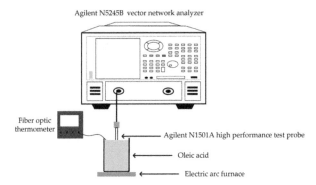

Figure 2. Complex permittivity measurement system.

Table 2. The complex permittivity of oleic at different temperatures.

Temperature	ε'	ε''
27 °C	2.563416	0.007422231
37 °C	2.572715	0.008652959
43 °C	2.577733	0.009912491
54 °C	2.564682	0.005191663
70 °C	2.566721	0.005631242

The mixture-averaged Looyenga and Landau, Lifshitz equation is given by [31]:

$$\varepsilon^{\frac{1}{3}}(i) = \sum_{i=s,w,g} v_i \varepsilon_i^{\frac{1}{3}}(i),\tag{6}$$

where v_i and ε_i are the volume fractions and dielectric properties of phase i, respectively. The volume fraction of solid, liquid water, and gas can be written in terms of total porosity. In this model, the v_i of oleic acid is 0.1, and the v_i of silicon carbide is 0.9.

The parameters of dynamic viscosity, conductivity, heat conductivity coefficient, heat capacity at constant pressure, and density are calculated by using the volume average method in this model.

2.1.4. Boundary Conditions

For the electromagnetic field, the left side of the waveguide is connected to a tunable short circuit. Since the microwave energy comes into the waveguide from the right, we can define it as a perfect electric conductor, except for the microwave feeding port. The mode of the electric field is TE_{10}. The meaning of TE (Transverse Electric wave) is a magnetic field in the direction of wave propagation without existing the electric field. There may be an infinite number of TM$_{mn}$ modes in the rectangular waveguide, and the waveform indexes m, n respectively represent the number of standing wave maximum value of the electromagnetic field along the broad side a and the narrow side b of the waveguide, and the lowest mode in the rectangular waveguide is the TE$_{10}$ mode.

The governing equation can be expressed as:

$$\vec{n} \times \vec{E} = 0,\tag{7}$$

where $\vec{n}$ is the unit normal vector of the corresponding surface.

For heat transfer, the initial inlet fluid into the tube's bottom temperature was set as 24 °C, which is the same as the room temperature.

For the free and porous media flow, a hydrodynamic no-slip boundary was used [32]. The bottom of the tube was set as an inlet, and constant velocities were set as 60 mL/min, 120 mL/min, and 180 mL/min in the model and experiment. The top of the glass tube was set as outflow. For this problem, the interface can be defined as:

$$P = P_0,$$

$$[\mu(\nabla \vec{u} + (\nabla \vec{u})^T) - \frac{2}{3}\mu(\nabla \vec{u}) \cdot \vec{I}] \cdot \vec{n} = 0,\tag{8}$$

where P is the liquid level pressure; and $\vec{u}$ is the inlet velocity. The pressure level at the outlet is used as a reference value.

2.1.5. Mesh Size

Appropriate mesh size is crucial for model simulation. When the grid size is halved, the discretization error may fall to a quarter, while the calculation time will increase by nearly 16 times and the storage requirement will increase by eight times [33]. In order to determine the appropriate mesh size in this model, the normalized power absorption (NPA) of the treated material has been used to complete mesh independent studies [14].

$$NPA = \frac{P_a}{P_f}.\tag{9}$$

where P_a is power absorbed by the processing materials, the P_f is power fed into the system. The NPA grid size changes are shown in Figure 3. The manual of the software QuickWave (QuickWave v6.0, QWED, Warsaw, Poland) recommends 12 cells per wavelength for grid-independent results, while other studies [34,35] indicate that 10 cells per wavelength are sufficient.

$$m_{meshsize} \leq \frac{c}{10f\sqrt{\varepsilon}}\tag{10}$$

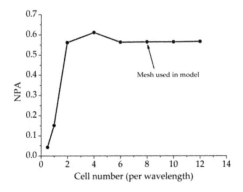

Figure 3. Normalized power absorption (NPA) variation of heating computations with different mesh sizes.

Here, both the NPA with mesh size and the calculation time are studied and shown in Figure 3. According to the mesh independent study, the mesh size used in this paper is defined as:

$$m_{meshsize} \leq \frac{c}{8f\sqrt{\varepsilon}}. \tag{11}$$

2.2. Experimental Setup

A schematic of the experimental system is shown in Figure 4. In this experiment, the microwave power is given by a solid-state power generator (WSPS-2450-200M, Wattsine, Chengdu, China). For power validation, an extra dual directional coupler is put into the experiment system. The microwave power was measured by a microwave power meter (AV2433, EI41, China Electronic Technology Instruments, Qingdao, China). Three different powers (200 W, 400 W, 600 W) with 2.45 GHz frequency were used to heat in this experiment. A glass tube (22 mm inner diameter and 26 mm outer diameter) was inserted through a BJ-22 waveguide with dimensions of 109.22 mm × 54.61 mm. The length of silicon carbide was 44 mm, and the diameter was 18 mm. The oleic acid flowed in glass tubes at three different flow velocities (60 mL/min, 120 mL/min, 180 mL/min), and the velocity of oleic acid was controlled by peristaltic pump (BT100-2J, Longer, Baoding, China). A fiber optical temperature sensor (FISO FOT-NS-967A, FISO Technologies, Quebec, QC, Canada) was employed to measure the temperature at two locations inside the pipe (A and B), as shown in Figure 3. Site B measured the temperature before the oleic acid was heated. Site A measured the temperature when the oleic acid was heated. Site A is 40 mm above the upper surface of the cavity. The position of the standing wave can be changed by adjusting the position of the short-circuit (HD-22WSS, Hengda Microwave, Xi'an, China) surface to achieve efficient use of microwave energy.

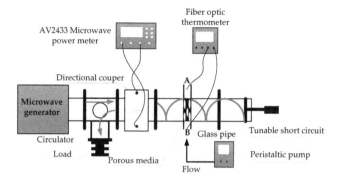

Figure 4. Schematic of experiment setup.

3. Results and Discussion

3.1. Experiment Validation

To complete the validation work of the simulation results and silicon carbide as a porous media, the solution was exposed to microwave and heated when it flowed into the microwave cavity via the porous media. Figure 5a–c shows the temperature rise of oleic acid at different microwave powers (200 W, 400 W, 600 W) and different oleic acid velocities (60 mL/min, 120 mL/min, 180 mL/min). The comparison demonstrates that the simulation results match the experiment results well.

The test result agrees well with the simulation. It can be seen from Figure 5 that microwave heating has a rapid heating effect, and it could reach a stable temperature state of heat exchange equilibrium within 150 s. In addition, the lower is the flow velocity, the higher is the temperature that can be achieved when the heat transfer effect reaches the stable liquid outflow.

From Figures 6 and 7, it is evident that uniform temperature distribution has been achieved. The problem that microwave cannot be heated uniformly is solved, which meets the requirement of heating oleic acid in the process of microwave-assisted biodiesel production.

Figure 8 presents the simulation result of temperature rise and microwave power loss density at different positions. It is obvious that the temperatures of both sides of oleic acid are lower than the center, and this is also the case with power loss density. This is consistent with the theory: a higher energy loss due to the absorption of microwave energy increases the temperature.

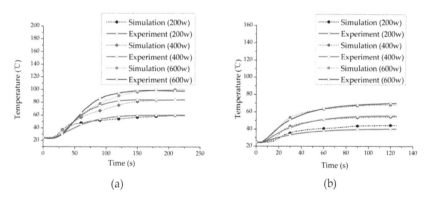

Figure 5. *Cont.*

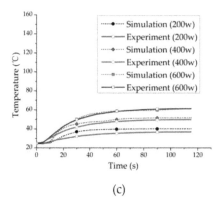

(c)

Figure 5. Temperature rise (°C) comparisons between the experiment and simulation: (**a**) temperature rise at a velocity of 60 mL/min; (**b**) temperature rise at a velocity of 120 mL/min; (**c**) temperature rise at a velocity of 180 mL/min.

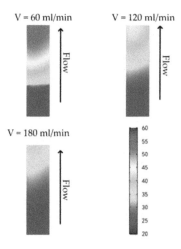

Figure 6. The cross-sectional temperature (°C) distribution at different velocities when the microwave power is 200 W in the simulation.

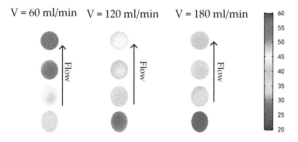

Figure 7. Temperature profile (°C) over different cross sections along the z-axis at different velocities when the microwave power is 200 W.

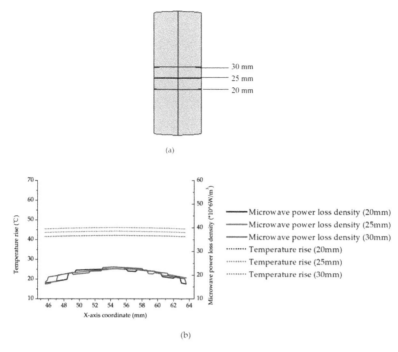

Figure 8. (**a**) Height position calibration; (**b**) The temperature rise (°C) profile and electromagnetic power loss density profile. The cross line from site (45.6, 150, Z) to site (63.6, 150, Z) at 200 W under 60 mL/min velocity (Z = 20 mm, 25 mm, 30 mm).

In order to verify the uniformity of heating, designing the experiment to measure the temperature at three points of the outflow. The positions of the three points are shown in Figure 9. The microwave power used in the experiment was 200 W, and the flow velocities were 60 mL/min, 120 mL/min, and 180 mL/min, for testing the uniformity of heating.

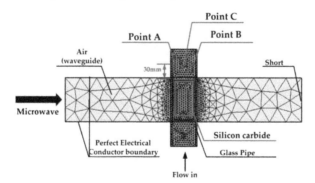

Figure 9. Identification of different temperature measurement points.

As can be seen from Figure 10, heating uniformity after flowing through the porous medium is basically improved. Moreover, the temperature increasing trends at the three temperature measuring points are consistent, and the temperature is approximately the same. When the temperature was measured, because the three fibers were very difficult to fix, the measured value exhibits small instability. However, the uniformity of microwave heating is essentially realized and can be utilized in practical industrial applications.

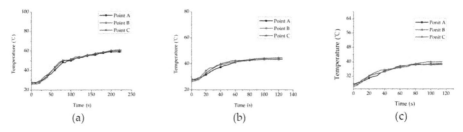

Figure 10. Temperature rise at point A (45.6, 150, 85), point B (54.6, 150, 85), and point C (63.6, 150, 85) when the microwave power was 200 W. (**a**) temperature rise at a velocity of 60 mL/min; (**b**) temperature rise at a velocity of 120 mL/min; and (**c**) temperature rise at a velocity of 180 mL/min.

3.2. Efficient Heating Method Optimization and Analysis

The effects of different sizes, porosities and materials on the S-parameters are now discussed, and the stable temperature is computed in simulation. S_{uv} is the relationship between input energy from the v port and the output energy from the u port. For example, S_{11} describes the signal reflected at port 1 for the signal incident at port 1.

The S_{11} calculation equation:

$$S_{11} = 10\lg(\frac{P_r}{P_i}),\tag{9}$$

where P_i represents the input power; and P_r is the reflected power.

Firstly, in the former simulation, the radii of the quartz tube is 11 mm. Different sizes of silicon carbide and tube are now considered. The S_{11} of different quartz tubes' radii and silicon carbide's radii are shown in Table 3. The height of silicon carbide is 54.6 mm in simulation, which is the same as BJ22 waveguide's height. In addition, the power is 200 W, and the velocity is 60 mL/min.

Table 3. The S_{11} and stable temperature of different quartz tubes' radii and silicon carbide's radii.

Quartz Tube's Radius (mm)	13	12	14	15	16	17	18	19	20
Silicon Carbide's Radius (mm)	11	11	12	13	14	15	16	17	18
S_{11} (dB)	−6.03	−6.48	−6.61	−6.96	−7.12	−6.95	−6.85	−6.62	−6.36
Stable Temperature (°C)	51.97	38.07	50.54	50.78	49.34	47.76	47.76	45.78	48.74

Next, considering the effect of quartz wall's thickness on S_{11}, the radius of silicon carbide is 14 mm.

Tables 3 and 4 show the S_{11} of different silicon carbide and quartz tube sizes. When the radius of silicon carbide is 14 mm and the tube's inner radius is 16 mm, the quartz's wall is 1 mm, and the S_{11} is −7.93 dB. According to the S_{11} calculation equation, approximately 84% of the microwave energy is absorbed. This could achieve the efficient use of microwave energy.

Thirdly, the effect of different porosities on microwave efficiency was analyzed. Table 5 presents the calculation result under the condition that microwave power is 200 W and oleic acid velocity is 60 mL/min. As shown in the table, the greater the porosity and the lower the amount of silicon carbide, the smaller the S_{11} and the higher the temperature when the heat transfer effect is balanced.

Table 4. The S_{11} and stable temperature of different quartz tube's thicknesses.

Quartz Tube's Radius (mm)	17	18	19	20	17	18	19
Quartz Tube's Inner Radius (mm)	15	16	17	18	16	16	16
Silicon Carbide's Radius (mm)	14	14	14	14	14	14	14
S_{11} (dB)	−7.78	−7.11	−6.35	−5.82	−7.93	−7.12	−6.18
Stable Temperature (°C)	38.79	49.34	55.56	54.98	52.36	49.34	44.87

Table 5. The S_{11} and temperature of different porosities of silicon carbide.

Porosity	0.45	0.6	0.75	0.9
S_{11} (dB)	−2.8	−3.54	−5.76	−7.24
Stable temperature (°C)	34.81	37.65	44.20	54.36

Figure 11 shows the temperature rise in a Y–Z cross section at different porosities when microwave power is 200 W and oleic acid velocity is 60 mL/min. As the porosity increases, S_{11} becomes smaller, more microwave energy is absorbed by silicon carbide, the temperature increase is larger, and the temperature of oleic acid increases. It is evident that a better heating effect can be achieved with a greater porosity.

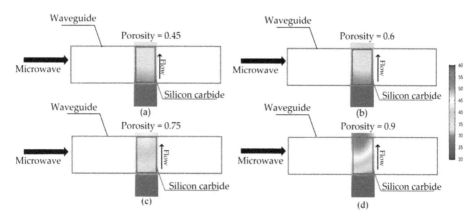

Figure 11. Temperature rise (°C) comparisons at different porosities in simulation. (**a**) temperature rise at porosity of 0.45; (**b**) temperature rise at porosity of 0.6; (**c**) temperature rise at porosity of 0.75; (**d**) temperature rise at porosity of 0.9.

Finally, silicon nitride was used for simulation. Silicon carbide and silicon nitride are dielectric loss absorbers. They are often utilized as ceramic absorbers [36]. Otherwise, silicon nitride has a good thermal stability and abrasion resistance [37]. The complex permittivity changes very little with temperature rising, so the dielectric constant of silicon nitride is calculated as constants here. Next, Figure 12a shows the simulation results for different power and velocities using silicon nitride. The heating effect was calculated at different porosities when the microwave power was 200 W and the velocity was 60 mL/min.

As shown in Figure 12, the temperature of oleic acid is higher in using silicon nitride than silicon carbide. The reason for this is that the dielectric loss of silicon nitride is greater, and the ability to absorb microwave is stronger. In future work, other materials with high dielectric loss can be used to heat oleic acid for microwave-assisted biodiesel production to achieve efficient uniform heating of microwaves.

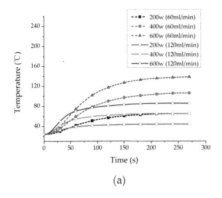 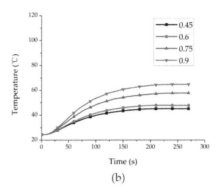

(a)   (b)

Figure 12. Temperature increase of oleic acid using silicon nitride under different conditions: (a) at different power and velocity; and (b) at different porosities.

4. Conclusions

This paper proposes a method for heating oleic acid by microwave to achieve the pretreatment of microwave-assisted biodiesel production. A general model to compute microwave heating in the fluid–solid coupling situation has been built and computed by COMSOL Multiphysics in the finite element method. An elaborate experimental system was developed to validate the multiphysics model. As a porous media, silicon carbide was utilized to complete the experimental verification. A good heating effect has been achieved. The test results are in good agreement with the simulation results. Moreover, the influence of different sizes, porosities, and materials on microwave absorption efficiency was calculated and used to provide guidance for the subsequent design of high efficiency microwave heating systems. This provides the requisite industrial guidelines for designing larger systems to heat oleic acid to realize large-scale microwave-assisted biodiesel production.

Author Contributions: H.Z. conceived and designed the experiments; W.M. developed the model, performed the experiments, analyzed the data, and wrote the initial draft of the manuscript; B.L., T.X., T.H., J.Z. and Y.Y. reviewed and contributed to the final manuscript; K.H. contributed the location and equipment.

Funding: This work was supported by the National Natural Science Foundation Youth Fund of China (Grant No. 61601312, 61501311). The Sichuan Science and Technology Program (Grant No. 2018FZ0008). State Key Laboratory of Efficient Utilization for Low Grade Phosphate Rock and Its Associated Resources (Grant No. WFKF2017-05).

Conflicts of Interest: The authors declare no conflict of interest.

References

1. Leadbeater, N.E.; Stencel, L.M. Fast, easy preparation of biodiesel using microwave heating. *Energy Fuels* **2006**, *20*, 2281–2283. [CrossRef]
2. Du, Z.; Li, Y.; Wang, X.; Wan, Y.; Chen, Q.; Wang, C.; Lin, X.; Liu, Y.; Chen, P.; Ruan, R. Microwave-assisted pyrolysis of microalgae for biofuel production. *Bioresour. Technol.* **2011**, *102*, 4890–4896. [CrossRef] [PubMed]
3. Yu, F.; Deng, S.B.; Chen, P.; Liu, Y.H.; Wan, Y.Q.; Olson, A. Physical and chemical properties of bio-oils from microwave pyrolysis of corn stover. *Appl. Biochem. Biotechnol.* **2007**, *137*, 957–970. [PubMed]
4. Miura, M.; Kaga, H.; Sakurai, A.; Kakuchi, T.; Takahashi, K. Rapid pyrolysis of wood block by microwave heating. *J. Anal. Appl. Pyrolysis* **2004**, *71*, 187–199. [CrossRef]
5. Vyas, A.P.; Verma, J.L.; Subrahmanyam, N. A review on fame production processes. *Fuel* **2010**, *89*, 1–9. [CrossRef]
6. Mansouri, S.S.; Ismail, M.I.; Babi, D.K.; Simasatitkul, L.; Huusom, J.K.; Gani, R. Systematic sustainable process design and analysis of biodiesel processes. *Processes* **2013**, *1*, 167–202. [CrossRef]
7. Lu, X.; Xi, B.; Zhang, Y.; Angelidaki, I. Microwave pretreatment of rape straw for bioethanol production: Focus on energy efficiency. *Bioresour. Technol.* **2011**, *102*, 7937–7940. [CrossRef] [PubMed]

8. Li, J.; Xiong, Q.; Wang, K.; Liang, S.; Gao, M. Combining sliding mode neural network with Cuckoo Search to make a uniform microwave heating process. *Int. J. Appl. Electron.* **2015**, *49*, 61–77. [CrossRef]
9. Mudgett, R.E. Microwave properties and heating characteristics of foods. *Food Technol.* **1986**, *40*, 84–87.
10. Muley, P.D.; Boldor, D. Multiphysics numerical modeling of the continuous flow microwave-assisted transesterification process. *J. Microw. Power Electromagn. Energy* **2016**, *46*, 139–162. [CrossRef]
11. Goldblith, S.A.; Wang, D.I.C. Effect of microwaves on *Escherichia coli* and *Bacillus subtilis*. *Appl. Microbiol.* **1967**, *15*, 1371–1375. [PubMed]
12. Huang, K.M.; Liao, Y.H. Transient power loss density of electromagnetic pulse in debye media. *IEEE Trans. Microw. Theory Tech.* **2015**, *63*, 135–140. [CrossRef]
13. Pandit, R.B.; Prasad, S. Finite element analysis of microwave heating of potato–Transient temperature profiles. *J. Food Eng.* **2003**, *60*, 193–202. [CrossRef]
14. Pitchai, K.; Birla, S.L.; Subbiah, J.; Jones, D.; Thippareddi, H. Coupled electromagnetic and heat transfer model for microwave heating in domestic ovens. *J. Food Eng.* **2012**, *112*, 100–111. [CrossRef]
15. Pitchai, K.; Chen, J.; Birla, S.; Gonzalez, R.; Jones, D.; Subbiah, J. A microwave heat transfer model for a rotating multicomponent meal in a domestic oven: Development and validation. *J. Food Eng.* **2014**, *128*, 60–71. [CrossRef]
16. Durlofsky, L.; Brady, J.F. Analysis of the brinkman equation as a model for flow in porous media. *Phys. Fluids* **1987**, *30*, 3329–3341. [CrossRef]
17. Rhodes, M.E. Transport in Heterogeneous Porous Media. Ph.D. Thesis, Imperial College London, London, UK, 2006.
18. Hwang, S.G.; ADvani, S.G. Numerical simulations of Stokes-Brinkman equations for permeability prediction of dual scale fibrous porous media. *Phys. Fluids* **2010**, *22*, 113101. [CrossRef]
19. Polyanin, A.D.; Aristov, S.N. A new method for constructing exact solutions to three-dimensional Navier-Stokes and Euler equations. *Theor. Found. Chem. Eng.* **2011**, *45*, 885–890. [CrossRef]
20. Jacimovic, N.; Hosoda, T.; Kishida, K.; Ivetic, M. Numerical solution of the Navier-Stokes equations for incompressible flow in porous media with free surface boundary. *J. Appl. Mech.* **2005**, *8*, 225–231. [CrossRef]
21. Drazin, P.G.; Riley, N. The Navier-Stokes equations. A classification of flows and exact solutions, Moduli Spaces. *J. Fluid Mech.* **2006**, *38*, 217–220.
22. Noureddini, H.; Teoh, B.C.; Clements, L.D. Viscosities of vegetable oils and fatty acids. *J. Am. Oil Chem. Soc.* **1992**, *69*, 1184–1188. [CrossRef]
23. Baroncini, C.; Filippo, P.D.; Latini, G.; Pacetti, M. Organic liquid thermal conductivity: A prediction method in the reduced temperature range 0.3 to 0.8. *Int. J. Thermophys.* **1981**, *2*, 21–38. [CrossRef]
24. Zhong, W.; Wu, M. Dieletric properties modeling studies of silicon nitride ceramic in high temperature. *Piezoelectr. Acoustoopt.* **2014**, *36*, 857–860.
25. Sun, X.; Liu, X.; Huang, L. Effects of TiN addition on mechanic properties and electroconductive of Si_3N_4 matrix materials. *J. Ceram.* **1999**, *20*, 196–189.
26. Wang, S. Fabrication and Properties of Si_3N_4/SiC Composites Ceramic. Master's Thesis, Wuhan University of Science and Technology, Wuhan, China, 2012.
27. Wu, M. Porous Dielectric Material Thermal Behavior Research. Master's Thesis, University of Electronic Science and Technology of China, Chengdu, China, 2016.
28. Motasemi, F.; Salema, A.A.; Afzal, M.T. Dielectric characterization of corn stover for microwave processing technology. *Fuel Process. Technol.* **2015**, *131*, 370–375. [CrossRef]
29. Alexandra, K.; Jan, D.; Pavol, S. Thermal shock resistance and fracture toughness of liquid-phase-sintered SiC-based ceramics. *J. Eur. Ceram. Soc.* **2009**, *29*, 2387–2394.
30. Liu, X.; Li, H.; Gao, X. Research progress of foam SiC ceramic materials. *Chem. Ind. Eng. Prog.* **2012**, *30*, 2520–2524.
31. Zhu, H.; Gulati, T.; Datta, A.K.; Huang, K. Microwave drying of spheres: Coupled electromagnetics-multiphase transport modeling with experimentation. Part I: Model development and experimental methodology. *Food. Bioprod. Process.* **2015**, *96*, 314–325. [CrossRef]
32. Zhu, J.; Kuznetsov, A.V.; Sandeep, K.P. Numerical simulation of forced convection in a duct subjected to microwave heating. *Heat Mass Transf.* **2006**, *43*, 255–264. [CrossRef]
33. Rylander, T.; Bondeson, A. Stable FEM-FDTD hybrid method for Maxwell's equations. *Comput Phys Commun.* **2000**, *125*, 75–82. [CrossRef]
34. Pathak, S.K.; Liu, F.; Tang, J. Finite difference time domain (FDTD) characterization of a single mode applicator. *J. Microw. Power Electromagn. Energy* **2016**, *38*, 37–48. [CrossRef]

35. Hong, Y.; Lin, B.; Li, H.; Dai, H.; Zhu, C.; Yao, H. Three-dimensional simulation of microwave heating coal sample with varying parameters. *Appl. Therm. Eng.* **2016**, *93*, 1145–1154. [CrossRef]
36. Qin, Q.; Zhang, Y.; Zhang, X. Research progress of microwave absorption materials. *Electron. Compon. Mater.* **2009**, *28*, 78–81.
37. Li, Y.; Yang, L.; Hong, L.; Yang, C.; Gao, J. Thermal stability of oxygen containing silicon nitride ceramic fibers in inert atmosphere. *Bull. Chin. Ceram. Soc.* **2015**, *34*, 1798–1802.

Article

Optimization of Microwave-Assisted Extraction of Essential Oil from Vietnamese Basil (*Ocimum basilicum* L.) Using Response Surface Methodology

Thien Hien Tran [1], Huynh Huu Hao Nguyen [2], Duy Chinh Nguyen [1], Thanh Quang Nguyen [1], Huynh Tan [1], Le Thi Hong Nhan [3], Dai Hai Nguyen [4,6], Lam Dai Tran [5,6], Sy Trung Do [7] and Trinh Duy Nguyen [1,*]

[1] NTT Hi-Tech Institute, Nguyen Tat Thanh University, 300A Nguyen Tat Thanh, District 4, Ho Chi Minh City 755414, Vietnam; hientran.cg@gmail.com (T.H.T.); ndchinh@ntt.edu.vn (D.C.N.); ntquang@ntt.edu.vn (T.Q.N.); htan@ntt.edu.vn (H.T.)

[2] Faculty of Chemical and Food Technology, Nguyen Tat Thanh University, 300A Nguyen Tat Thanh, District 4, Ho Chi Minh City 755414, Vietnam; haonguyen190495@gmail.com

[3] Department of Chemical Engineering, HCMC University of Technology, VNU-HCM, Ho Chi Minh City 700000, Vietnam; lthnhan@hcmut.edu.vn

[4] Institute of Applied Materials Science, Vietnam Academy of Science and Technology, Ho Chi Minh City 700000, Vietnam; nguyendaihai0511@gmail.com

[5] Institute for Tropical Technology, Vietnam Academy of Science and Technology, 18 Hoang Quoc Viet, Cau Giay District, Hanoi 10072, Vietnam; trandailam@gmail.com

[6] Graduate University of Science and Technology, Vietnam Academy of Science and Technology, 18 Hoang Quoc Viet, Cau Giay District, Hanoi 10072, Vietnam

[7] Institute of Chemistry, Vietnam Academy of Science and Technology, 18 Hoang Quoc Viet, Cau Giay District, Hanoi 10072, Vietnam; dosyvhh@gmail.com

* Correspondence: ndtrinh@ntt.edu.vn

Received: 27 September 2018; Accepted: 23 October 2018; Published: 25 October 2018

Abstract: Basil plant is a common source for linalool and estragole. However, it has been showed that the chemical composition of basil varies considerably depending on many factors including method of extraction, cultivar of the plant or geographical location. In this study, we attempted to extract essential oil from Vietnamese basil and analyze the chemical composition of the obtained oil using gas chromatography–mass spectrometry (GC-MS). The extraction method of choice was microwave-assisted hydro-distillation (MAHD) and the process was optimized with Response Surface Methodology (RSM) with regard to four experimental parameters including raw material size, raw material to water ratio, extraction time and microwave power. The results showed that ground basil leaves, when extracted with optimal conditions of water-to-material ratio of 3.2:1, extraction time of 97 (min) and microwave power of 430 (W), gave the actual essential oil yield of 0.6%. Regarding ANOVA results of the quadratic model, high determination coefficient ($R^2 = 0.9077$), significant F-value of 10.92 and the p-value of less than 0.05 indicate that this model is significant between experimental and predicted variables, and should be fixed. In addition, GC-MS analysis revealed that major components of Vietnamese Basil were Estragole (87.869%), α-Bergamotene (2.922%), τ-Cadinol (2.770%), and Linalool (1.347%).

Keywords: Basil (*Ocimum basilicum* L.); microwave-assisted extraction; response surface methodology; yield and composition of essential oils

---

1. Introduction

Substances derived from plant ingredients, especially essential oils, have been extensively used in many industries including cosmetics, food and pharmaceuticals [1]. Essential oils are complex, volatile compounds characterized by strong odors. The chemical composition of the essential oil is derived from terpenes and oxidizing compounds, or fatty compounds, in which each of these compounds produce different properties of essential oils [2].

Ocimum basilicum L., commonly referred to as basil, is a plant that belongs to the Lamiaceae family [3]. Basil is native to India and China due to the favorable climatic conditions, but is now commonly cultivated in many tropical and temperate countries in Asia, Africa, Central and South America [4]. In fresh form, basil leaf is often used as a daily spice and food ingredient. In traditional medicine, thanks to the anti-inflammatory, anti-oxidant and antimicrobial properties of the plant, basil is also used to promote digestion, stimulate respiratory circulation, relieve cold symptoms and alleviate digestion issues [5].

The essential oils extracted from basil organs are of light yellow color with a subtle aroma [6]. Similar to the fresh plant and basil-derived products, basil essential oils also exhibited numerous valuable pharmaceutical properties, most notably antimicrobial and anti-fungal activities [7–11]. Regarding chemical composition, basil oil is a complex mixture composed of many chemical components, few of which are found at relatively high concentrations including citral, 1,8-cineole, linalool, estragole, eugenol, methyl eugenol and methyl cinnamate [12]. However, empirical investigations have shown that chemical compositions of basil vary considerably. For example, while basil leaves collected in Turkey and Iran were found to be abundantly composed of estragole (52.6% in Basil sample obtained in Turkey, 52.4% and 40.4% in Iranian purple basil leaves and in green basil leaves respectively) [13,14], other studies indicated that other cultivars such as Brazilian and Pakistani leaves contain mostly linalool with concentrations ranging from 56.7 to 69.3% [10,15]. Such differences with regard to composition could be due to various factors, including seasonal variation [10], geographical location of the plant, extraction method [16] and most strikingly, cultivar of the basil [17].

When it comes to extracting essentials oils from plant materials, apart from the conventional hydro-distillation method (HD) used in the aforementioned composition studies of basil, microwave-assisted hydro-distillation (MAHD) has recently been considered as a preferable method due to advantages over conventional ones regarding cost and time effectiveness, environmental friendliness and reduced energy consumption [18]. In addition, microwave-assisted methods in essential oil extraction could improve both the yield and quality of the produced oils. This enhancement effect is attributable to the internal pressure inside the oil gland cell wall exerted by microwave energy, which effectively leaches out the oil contained inside [18]. Similar to HD, the MAHD process also requires careful selection of experimental parameters. However, most studies for basil generally compare results of solvent-free microwave extraction (SFME) with HD extraction [16,19] or analyze chemical composition of Basil oils after HD extraction, and therefore, lack rigorous optimization for the extraction process. An exception to this is one particular work where MAHD processing of Mexican basil is optimized with Response Surface Methodology (RSM) [20]. However, chemical composition of the basil extract was not clearly reported in this study.

Given these notions, the aim of this study is two-fold. First, we continue this research direction by adopting MAHD process to extract essential oils from another basil cultivar, Vietnamese basil, as to the best of our knowledge, the essential oil extraction of this plant has not yet been attempted. In addition, to achieve the maximum oil yield, Response Surface Methodology (RSM) is applied. RSM is a technique that is widely utilized in optimization of many processes including removal of contaminants from wastewater [21–25], extraction of natural compounds from plants [26–28] or gelatin from animal by-products [29]. In this study, optimization of the extraction process is conducted with regard to three parameters including water-to-material ratio, microwave power and extraction time. Second, by examining chemical composition of the extracted Vietnamese Basil essential oils, we compare that with other studies to propose the use of Vietnamese basil in possible large scale production.

2. Materials and Methods

2.1. Plant Sample Preparation

Fresh basil leaves of approximately 3 cm were purchased in the local market in Go Vap District, Ho Chi Minh City, Vietnam. After purchasing, the materials were washed with water several times to remove impurities. All raw materials are stored in a desiccant bag, stored in a refrigerator (LC-1416B, Alaska, Ho Chi Minh City, Vietnam) at temperatures below 10 °C.

2.2. Extraction Method

The system for basil oil extraction comprises a domestic microwave oven (model ME71A, Samsung, Ho Chi Minh City, Vietnam), acting as the heat source for extraction, and a Clevenger distillation apparatus (Bach Khoa Ltd., Ho Chi Minh City, Vietnam). The flask containing the plant material is placed inside the oven cavity and is connected to the apparatus outside the oven for condensing and separating the oil and aqueous phase.

2.3. Extraction Process

The process of basil essential oil extraction is shown in Figure 1. First, fresh basil leaves were washed, then cut into pieces with size of around 1 cm or ground in accordance with the experiment. The processed sample was then weighed to 100 g with an electronic scale and introduced into the 1 L flask containing water following a pre-specified water-to-raw ratio. Following that, Clevenger extraction was conducted by the microwave oven. Time is measured immediately after turning the oven on. After the extraction period, the raw essential oil is removed and a small amount of condensate is obtained. Lastly, the extracted oil is dried with Na_2SO_4 (Sigma-Aldrich, St. Louis, MO, USA) to completely remove the remaining condensate.

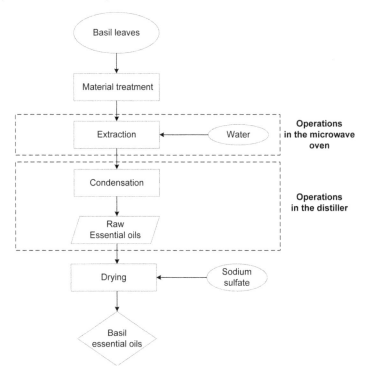

Figure 1. *Cont.*

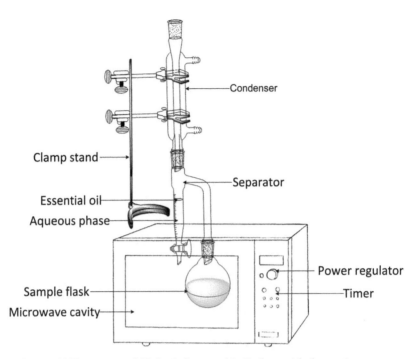

Figure 1. (a) The process and **(b)** sketch diagram of the Basil essential oil extraction process.

2.4. Optimization of the Extraction Process Using RSM Procedure

First, we conduct single factor investigation of four factors including material size, water-to-material ratio, time, and microwave power by individually varying one factor while keeping other variables at a fixed value. Based on our acquaintance with the basil essential oil, fixed values were chosen as water-to-material ratio of 3:1, 60 min of extraction time and 450 W of microwave power. Obtained set of values by single factor investigation will then be used in Central Composite Design (CCD) to produce multiple sets of experiment conditions (See Tables 1 and 2. For CCD results). Following that, 20 experiment attempts will be conducted following the specified conditions to generate the oil yield data for estimation of a second-order quadratic model. Estimation results will be tested with ANOVA (Analysis of Variance) to confirm model validity. Lastly, optimal conditions are calculated from the final model and verified by an actual experiment attempt.

Essential oil yield, measured in %, is determined from the following the formula: $Y = \frac{V}{m} \times 100$, where V and m are volume of attained oil (mL) and weight of used basil leaves (g) respectively. CCD, ANOVA and calculation of optimal conditions were executed using Design-Expert software (Stat-ease Inc., Minneapolis, MN, USA). All experimental attempts were conducted in triplicate where the highest value would be recorded.

Table 1. Levels and Independent factors of the basil essential oil extraction process.

	Independent Factors		
Levels	Ratio of Water and Basil Leaves A (mL/g)	Extraction Time B (min)	Microwave Power C (W)
$-\alpha$	1.32:1	39.55	197.73
-1	2:1	60	300
0	3:1	90	450
1	4:1	120	600
$+\alpha$	4.68:1	140.45	702.27

Table 2. Details of experimental attempts employed in the Response Surface Methodology (RSM) optimization.

No.	Parameters			Yields		No.	Parameters			Yields	
	Ratio (A)	Time (B)	Power (C)	Actual	Predicted		Ratio (A)	Time (B)	Power (C)	Actual	Predicted
1	2	60	300	0.40	0.38	11	3	39.5	450	0.40	0.41
2	4	60	300	0.50	0.49	12	3	140	450	0.50	0.53
3	2	120	300	0.50	0.49	13	3	90	198	0.50	0.53
4	4	120	300	0.60	0.57	14	3	90	702	0.50	0.51
5	2	60	600	0.40	0.41	15	3	90	450	0.70	0.67
6	4	60	600	0.50	0.48	16	3	90	450	0.70	0.67
7	2	120	600	0.50	0.67	17	3	90	450	0.70	0.67
8	4	120	600	0.50	0.50	18	3	90	450	0.60	0.67
9	1.32	90	450	0.40	0.41	19	3	90	450	0.60	0.67
10	4.68	90	450	0.50	0.53	20	3	90	450	0.70	0.67

2.5. Identification of Components by Gas Chromatography-Mass Spectrometry (GC-MS)

To determine the chemical composition in the oil sample, 25 µL of essential oil taken from the optimized process was mixed in 1.0 mL n-hexane and dehydrated with Na_2SO_4. The instrument was GC Agilent 6890 N (Agilent Technologies, Santa Clara, CA, USA), MS 5973 inert, HP5-MS column, head column pressure of 9.3 psi. GC-MS were obtained under the following conditions: carrier gas He; flow rate 1.0 mL/min; split 1:100; injection volume 1.0 µL; injection temperature 250 °C. From the initial hold at 50 °C for 2 min, oven temperature progressed to 80 °C at 2 °C/min, from 80 °C to 150 °C at 5 °C/min, from 150 °C to 200 °C at 10 °C/min, from 200 °C to 300 °C at 20 °C/min and was maintained at 300 °C for 5 min.

3. Results and Discussion

3.1. Single Factor Investigation

The factors that affect the yield of basil essential oil in the extraction process are shown in Figure 2. Figure 2a indicated that the yield of basil essential oil increased as the material size decreases. When the basil leaves size changes from whole to ground leaves, the yield of the essential oil increases from 0.2 to 0.5%. This decline could be explained as follows. As the material is cut smaller, cells containing the oil are broken in larger quantities, making water diffusing into the oil sacs of basil more quickly. This rapidly pushes the essential oils out under the influence of microwave energy, leading to higher performance. Therefore, ground basil leaves have been chosen in subsequent investigations.

In the second survey, the water-to-material ratio factor was investigated. From Figure 2b, the extract yield increased from 0.2 to 0.5% when increasing the ratio from 1:1 to 3:1. Since water is absorbed into the material easily, ingredients could be dissolved more efficiently with higher amount of solvent. Therefore, adding more water to extraction process would cause greater diffusion of essential oil into the water, leading to increased yield of the essential oils. However, increasing this ratio from 3:1 to 4:1 caused the yield of the essential oil to decrease from 0.5 to 0.4% because excess water could dissolve or emulsify the oil. Therefore, the ratio of water to raw materials of 3:1 (mL/g) is selected for the best result of 0.5% yield for subsequent experiments.

Similarly, Figure 2c shows the time extraction effect to the yield of basil essential oil. When the extraction time increases from 30 to 90 min, the yield of the extracted essential oil gradually increases from 0.2 to 0.7% at 90 min, but it decreased to 0.4% at 105 min because of denaturation of some substances in the oil caused by prolonged exposure with high temperature. Regarding the effect of microwave power, Figure 2d shows that high microwave power leads to better performance of the extraction, but only to a certain extent, where corresponding yield would decrease thereafter. Increased temperature, caused by microwave-induced movement of molecules, could affect oil yield in two ways. First, magnetic wave heats water within the cells, exerting internal pressure and rupturing oil glands. Second, high temperature also impairs the surface tension and, in turn, viscosity of water, causing quicker heat transfer from outside into the materials. However, at a very high temperature, some temperature-sensitive substances in the essential oil could decompose, adversely affecting the extraction yield, the oil quality, and the cost of production due to the increased consumption of energy. Therefore, the extraction time and microwave power in the survey were chosen as 90 min and 450 W, respectively.

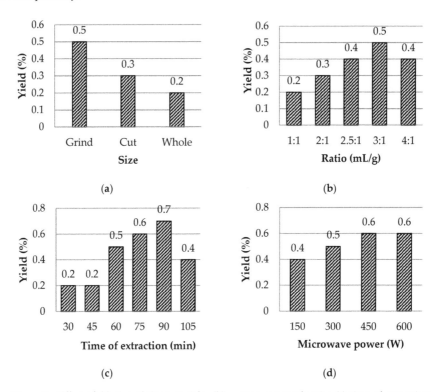

Figure 2. Effect of (a) size of the materials; (b) water-to-material ratio; (c) time of extraction; and (d) microwave power to the yield of the essential oil.

3.2. Optimization of Experimental Conditions Using RSM

Table 3 displayed the results of ANOVA for the second order regression model of extracted basil essential oil from which three factors were considered and analyzed. The F-mode value of 10.92 implied that the model produced by Design-Expert software is significant. There is only a 0.04% chance that an F-value this large could occur due to noise. *p*-values less than 0.0500 indicated that model terms are significant. In this case, A, B, A^2, B^2, C^2 are significant model terms. The Lack of Fit F-value of 0.42 implies the Lack of Fit is not significant relative to the pure error. There is an 81.67% chance that a Lack of Fit F-value this large could occur due to noise. The R^2 of 0.6895 is in reasonable agreement with the Adjusted R^2 of 0.8246. The Adeq. Precision of 9.4159 indicates an adequate signal and this model can be used to navigate the design space. Therefore, no further specification of the model is required and it can be asserted that the yield of the extraction model produced by the software is fixed and suitable. In addition, the experimental model was considered reasonably fit since calculated residuals follow a random pattern as shown in Figure 3a. Figure 3b demonstrated that data points corresponding to predicted and actual values were scattered across the 45-degree line with close proximity, suggesting that the actual results are accurately predicted from the factor values. Thus, based on the data analysis of the oil yield from experiments, the optimization of the predicted model results in optimized parameters as $A = 3.237{:}1$ (mL/g), $B = 97.074$ (min), and $C = 430.870$ (W), obtaining the yield of 0.674% with 90.77% reliability. The final quadratic model is described as follows:

$$Y = 0.6656 + 0.0343A + 0.0343B - 0.0073C - 0.0125AB - 0.0125AC - 0.0125BC - 0.0696A^2 - 0.0696B^2 - 0.0520C^2 \quad (1)$$

Table 3. ANOVA for the quadratic model.

Source	Sum of Squares	Df	Mean Square	F-Value	p-Value	Remarks
Model	0.1865	9	0.0207	10.92	0.0004	significant
Water-to-material Ratio (A)	0.016	1	0.016	8.46	0.0156	significant
Extraction time (B)	0.016	1	0.016	8.46	0.0156	significant
Microwave Power (C)	0.0007	1	0.0007	0.386	0.5483	not significant
AB	0.0013	1	0.0013	0.6589	0.4359	not significant
AC	0.0013	1	0.0013	0.6589	0.4359	not significant
BC	0.0013	1	0.0013	0.6589	0.4359	not significant
A^2	0.0699	1	0.0699	36.85	0.0001	significant
B^2	0.0699	1	0.0699	36.85	0.0001	significant
C^2	0.0389	1	0.0389	20.52	0.0011	significant
Residual	0.019	10	0.0019	-	-	-
Lack of Fit	0.0056	5	0.0011	0.4229	0.8167	not significant
Pure Error	0.0133	5	0.0027	-	-	-
Std. Dev.	0.0436	-	R^2	0.9077	-	-
Mean	0.535	-	Adjusted R^2	0.8246	-	-
C.V. (%)	8.14	-	Predicted R^2	0.6895	-	-
-	-	-	Adeq. Precision	9.4159	-	-

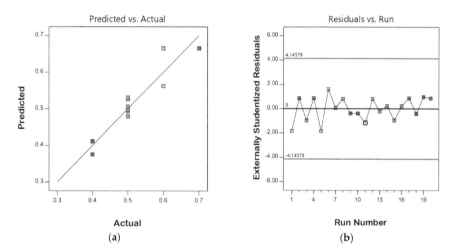

(a)   (b)

Figure 3. (a) The plot comparing actual values and predicted yield values; (b) Normal plot of Residuals with Run number. Points denoted as square dots correspond to actual experiment runs. Blue, cyan, green, and red color represent increasing order of actual yields corresponding to presented data points.

Based on the optimized parameters, Figure 4 shows the mutual interactions of the factors and interaction of factors with the yield of the lemon oil obtained. Visually, the efficiency of the attained oil increases proportionally with condition parameters. However, as these conditions exceed the optimal point (3.237:1 mL/g, 97.074 min, and 430.870 W), the obtained basil essential oil content ceases to rise, and eventually, starts diminishing. The parameters predicted by the software were then used to perform actual extraction for verification. After a set of triplicate experiments, the yield is determined at 0.6% which approximates the predicted yield from the model (0.674%). Given this result, it is suggested that empirical values were accurately predicted by the quadratic model.

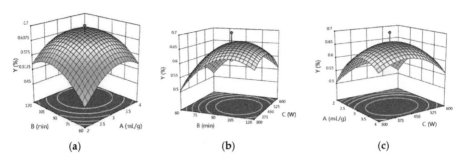

Figure 4. The 3D plots representing factors influencing yields of basil essential oil include (**a**) effect of extraction time and ratio; (**b**) effect of extraction time and microwave power; and (**c**) effect of ratio and microwave power.

Regarding yield, comparison of yields in various studies was showed in Table 4. We found that optimized yield derived from Vietnamese basil leaves (0.6%) was higher than optimized yield derived from MAHD extraction of Mexican basil leaf (0.45%). In comparison with studies of SFME with no optimization, our yield was also higher. However, it is inconclusive as to whether or not MAHD is more efficient than HD, in regard to basil oil extraction, since the reported yields for HD extraction varied wildly and were at variance with MAHD yields.

Table 4. Comparison of oil yields.

	This Study	[10]	[13]	[16]	[17]	[19]	[20]
Method	MAHD	HD	HD	SFME, HD	HD	SFME, HD	MAHD
Materials	Vietnamese leaves	Pakistani leaves	Turkish leaves	French leaves	Italian leaves	Egyptian leaves	Mexican leaves
Yield (%)	0.6	0.5 to 0.8 depending on seasonal variations	1.00	0.028 for SFME, 0.029 for HD	0.3 to 0.8 depending on shape, color and size of leaves	0.48 for both methods	0.45

3.3. Results of GC-MS

The results of GC-MS analyses revealing composition of essential oil are given in Table 5 and GC-MS chromatogram obtained for a sample of basil essential oil is illustrated in Figure 5. At first glance, it is indicated that the Vietnamese basil leaf was rich in estragole, as demonstrated by very high estragole content, at 87.9%, which is followed by α-Bergamotene, τ-cadinol and linalool respectively at 2.922%; 2.770% and 1.347%. Besides genetic differences and nutritional status of the plants, the abundance of estragole constituent in the oil could be explained by the effect of microwave. To be specific, microwave radiation causes polar molecules containing oxygen, such as water and estragole molecules, to spin rapidly. As such, polar compounds in oil bags could easily be separated from the material, leading to higher content. In contrast, hydrocarbons, which are nonpolar, are less prone to magnetic wave and are therefore less likely to be isolated [30]. For α-Bergamotene, τ-Cadinol and linalool, GC-MS results indicated that the presence of these substances is consistent with results from French, Italian, Egyptian and Iranian basil plants. Overall, the abundance of estragole suggests that Vietnamese basil leaf is a suitable material for production of flavoring and smelling agents.

Table 5. Constituents of the extracted essential oil and comparison with those of several studies relating to basil oil extraction.

R.T (min)	Constituent	Content (This Study)	[15] HD Brazilian Leaves	[10] HD Pakistani Leaves	[13] HD Turkish Leaves	[16] SFME, HD French Leaves	[17] HD Italian Leaves	[19] SFME, HD Egyptian Leaves	[14] HD Iranian Aerials
						Comparison with Regard to Method of Extraction, Material and Composition			
11.988	Limonene	0.254	nd	tr to 0.3	13.64	nd	nd to 0.58	nd	nd
12.103	1,8-Cineole	0.239	3.55	0.2 to 1.1	nd	1.5 to 5.8	0.9 to 12.9	6.8 to 7.3	nd to 2.4
16.380	Linalool	1.347	69.33	56.7 to 60.6	nd	25.3 to 39.1	41.1 to 76.2	43.5 to 48.4	nd to 20.1
18.680	L-camphor	0.290	nd	1.1 to 3.1	nd	0.3	0.10 to 0.83	0.3 to 0.4	nd
21.713	Estragole	87.869	nd	nd	52.60	nd	nd to 41.40	13.3 to 14.3	40.5 to 52.4
22.392	Fenchyl acetate	0.379	nd	nd	12.29	nd	nd to 0.56	0.1 to 0.2	nd
24.912	Acetic acid	0.217	nd	nd	nd	nd	nd	nd	nd
28.384	β-Elemene	0.693	nd	nd	nd	2.4 to 3.2	nd	0.7 to 0.9	nd
29.189	Caryophyllene	0.246	nd	1.2 to 1.7	nd	nd	0.12 to 0.66	0.1	nd
29.681	α-Bergamotene	2.922	nd	nd	nd	6.0 to 7.6	0.09 to 0.80	2.5 to 2.7	0.5 to 5.2
29.764	α-Guaiene	0.167	nd	nd	nd	nd	nd to 3.37	tr	nd
30.183	α-Caryophyllene	0.292	nd	nd	nd	nd	nd to 0.27	nd	nd
30.967	Germacrene-D	0.205	nd	1.1 to 3.3	0.47	nd	0.72 to 2.11	0.8 to 0.9	nd to 0.8
31.072	β-Farnesene	0.234	nd	nd	nd	nd	nd	0.4	nd
31.615	α-Bulnesene	0.302	1.07	nd	nd	nd	nd	nd	nd
31.824	γ-Cadinene	0.991	1.58	3.2 to 5.4	nd	2.2 to 3.1	0.38 to 1.37	1.1 to 1.3	nd to 1.8
33.236	(−)-Spathulenol	0.213	nd	tr to 0.5	nd	nd	nd	0.4 to 0.6	nd to 0.9
33.947	Cubenol	0.370	nd	nd	nd	nd	nd	nd	nd
34.407	τ-Cadinol	2.770	nd	nd	nd	5.6 to 6.7	1.76 to 7.55	0.1	nd to 5.9

nd: not detected. tr: trace amounts.

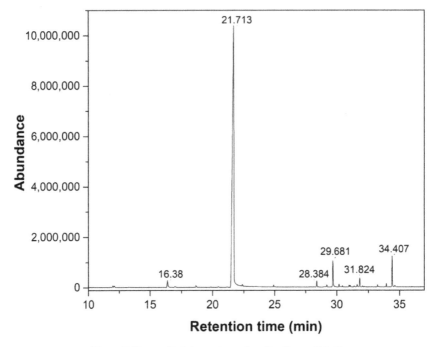

Figure 5. The result of chromatography of basil essential oil.

4. Conclusions

We have successfully applied and optimized MAHD extraction of essential oils from Vietnamese basil leaves. Results from RSM suggested that optimal conditions for this extraction include water to basil ratio of 3.237:1 (mL/g) time of extraction of 97.074 (min), and microwave power of 430.087 (W). After verifying the predicted optimal yield, we determined that the actual yield is 0.6%, which is higher than results of related studies applying MAHD and SFME. GC-MS results also revealed that Vietnamese basil is very rich in estragole. Therefore, it is possible to assert that the combination of RSM and microwave distillation makes the research direction faster, more economical and efficient than traditional methods.

Author Contributions: Data curation, L.T.H.N.; Formal analysis, T.Q.N.; Investigation, T.H.T., H.H.H.N., H.T. and L.T.H.N; Methodology, D.H.N.; Supervision, D.H.N., L.D.T. and T.D.N.; Visualization, S.T.D.; Writing–original draft, T.H.T. and D.C.N.; Writing–review and editing, D.C.N.

Funding: This research received no external funding.

Acknowledgments: The authors acknowledge Nguyen Tat Thanh University for providing facilities, chemicals, and permission during the research period.

Conflicts of Interest: The authors declare no conflicts of interest.

References

1. Rezvanpanah, S.; Rezaei, K.; Razavi, S.H.; Moini, S. Use of Microwave-assisted Hydrodistillation to Extract the Essential Oils from Satureja hortensis and Satureja montana. *Food Sci. Technol. Res.* **2008**, *14*, 311–314. [CrossRef]
2. Da Silva Gündel, S.; Velho, M.C.; Diefenthaler, M.K.; Favarin, F.R.; Copetti, P.M.; De Oliveira Fogaça, A.; Ourique, A.F. Basil oil-nanoemulsions: Development, cytotoxicity and evaluation of antioxidant and antimicrobial potential. *J. Drug Deliv. Sci. Technol.* **2018**, *46*, 378–383. [CrossRef]

3. Pushpangadan, P.; George, V. *Basil. Handbook of Herbs and Spices*, 2nd ed.; Woodhead Publishing: Cambridge, UK, 2012; Volume 1, pp. 55–72.

4. Kusuma, H.S.; Mahfud, M. Preliminary study: Kinetics of oil extraction from basil (*Ocimum basilicum*) by microwave-assisted hydrodistillation and solvent-free microwave extraction. *S. Afr. J. Chem.* **2016**, *21*, 49–53. [CrossRef]

5. Izadiyan, P.; Hemmateenejad, B. Multi-response optimization of factors affecting ultrasonic assisted extraction from Iranian basil using central composite design. *Food Chem.* **2016**, *190*, 864–870. [CrossRef] [PubMed]

6. Mindaryani, A.; Rahayu, S.S. Essential Oil from Extraction and Steam Distillation of Ocimum Basillicum. *World Congr. Eng. Comput. Sci.* **2007**, 4–8.

7. Snežana, F. Basil (*Ocimum basilicum* L.) a Source of Valuable Phytonutrients. *Int. J. Clin. Nutr. Dietetics* **2017**, *3*, 118–123.

8. Wan, J.; Wilcock, A.; Coventry, M.J. The effect of essential oils of basil on the growth of Aeromonas hydrophila and Pseudomonas fluorescens. *J. Appl. Microbiol.* **1998**, *84*, 152–158. [CrossRef] [PubMed]

9. Koba, K.; Poutouli, P.W.; Raynaud, C.; Chaumont, J.P.; Sanda, K. Chemical composition and antimicrobial properties of different basil essential oils chemotypes from Togo. *Bangladesh J. Pharmacol* **2009**, *4*, 1–8. [CrossRef]

10. Hussain, A.I.; Anwar, F.; Sherazi, S.T.H.; Przybylski, R. Chemical composition, antioxidant and antimicrobial activities of basil (*Ocimum basilicum*) essential oils depends on seasonal variations. *Food Chem.* **2008**, *108*, 986–995. [CrossRef] [PubMed]

11. Edris, A.E.; Farrag, E.S. Antifungal activity of peppermint and sweet basil essential oils and their major aroma constituents on some plant pathogenic fungi from the vapor phase. *Food/Nahrung* **2003**, *47*, 117–121. [CrossRef] [PubMed]

12. Koroch, A.R.; Simon, J.E.; Juliani, H.R. Essential oil composition of purple basils, their reverted green varieties (*Ocimum basilicum*) and their associated biological activity. *Ind. Crops Prod.* **2017**, *107*, 526–530. [CrossRef]

13. Chalchat, J.C.; Özcan, M.M. Comparative essential oil composition of flowers, leaves and stems of basil (*Ocimum basilicum* L.) used as herb. *Food Chem.* **2008**, *110*, 501–503. [CrossRef] [PubMed]

14. Sajjadi, S.E. Analysis of the essential oils of two cultivated Basil (*Ocimum basilicum* L.) from Iran. *DARU J. Pharm. Sci.* **2006**, *14*, 128–130.

15. De Almeida, I.; Alviano, D.S.; Vieira, D.P.; Alves, P.B.; Blank, A.F.; Lopes, A.H.C.; Maria do Socorro, S.R. Antigiardial activity of *Ocimum basilicum* essential oil. *Parasitol. Res.* **2007**, *101*, 443–452. [CrossRef] [PubMed]

16. Lucchesi, M.E.; Chemat, F.; Smadja, J. Solvent-free microwave extraction of essential oil from aromatic herbs: Comparison with conventional hydro-distillation. *J. Chromatogr. A* **2004**, *1043*, 323–327. [CrossRef] [PubMed]

17. Marotti, M.; Piccaglia, R.; Giovanelli, E. Differences in essential oil composition of basil (*Ocimum basilicum* L.) Italian cultivars related to morphological characteristics. *J. Agric. Food Chem.* **1996**, *44*, 3926–3929. [CrossRef]

18. Nitthiyah, J.; Nour, A.H.; Kantasamy, R.; Akindoyo, J.O. Microwave Assisted Hydrodistillation–An Overview of Mechanism and Heating Properties. *Aust. J. Basic Appl. Sci.* **2017**, *11*, 22–29.

19. Chenni, M.; El Abed, D.; Rakotomanomana, N.; Fernandez, X.; Chemat, F. Comparative study of essential oils extracted from Egyptian basil leaves (*Ocimum basilicum* L.) using hydro-distillation and solvent-free microwave extraction. *Molecules* **2016**, *21*, 113. [CrossRef] [PubMed]

20. Cardoso-Ugarte, G.A.; Juárez-Becerra, G.P.; SosaMorales, M.E.; López-Malo, A. Microwave-assisted extraction of essential oils from herbs. *J. Microw. Power Electromagn. Energy* **2013**, *47*, 63–72. [CrossRef] [PubMed]

21. Bezerra, M.A.; Santelli, R.E.; Oliveira, E.P.; Villar, L.S.; Escaleira, L.A. Response surface methodology (RSM) as a tool for optimization in analytical chemistry. *Talanta* **2008**, *76*, 965–977. [CrossRef] [PubMed]

22. Van Tran, T.; Bui, Q.T.P.; Nguyen, T.D.; Thanh Ho, V.T.; Bach, L.G. Application of response surface methodology to optimize the fabrication of $ZnCl_2$-activated carbon from sugarcane bagasse for the removal of Cu^{2+}. *Water Sci. Technol.* **2017**, *75*, 2047–2055. [CrossRef] [PubMed]

23. Van Tran, T.; Bui, Q.T.P.; Nguyen, T.D.; Le, N.T.H.; Bach, L.G. A comparative study on the removal efficiency of metal ions (Cu^{2+}, Ni^{2+}, and Pb^{2+}) using sugarcane bagasse-derived $ZnCl_2$-activated carbon by the response surface methodology. *Adsorpt. Sci. Technol.* **2017**, *35*, 72–85. [CrossRef]

24. Tran, V.T.; Nguyen, D.T.; Ho, V.T.T.; Hoang, P.Q.H.; Bui, P.Q.; Bach, L.G. Efficient removal of Ni^{2+} ions from aqueous solution using activated carbons fabricated from rice straw and tea waste. *J. Mater. Environ. Sci.* **2017**, *8*, 426–437.

25. Bach, L.G.; Van Tran, T.; Nguyen, T.D.; Van Pham, T.; Do, S.T. Enhanced adsorption of methylene blue onto graphene oxide-doped XFe_2O_4 (X = Co, Mn, Ni) nanocomposites: kinetic, isothermal, thermodynamic and recyclability studies. *Res. Chem. Intermed.* **2018**, *44*, 1661–1687. [CrossRef]

26. Silva, E.M.; Rogez, H.; Larondelle, Y. Optimization of extraction of phenolics from Inga edulis leaves using response surface methodology. *Sep. Purif. Technol.* **2007**, *55*, 381–387. [CrossRef]

27. Wang, S.; Chen, F.; Wu, J.; Wang, Z.; Liao, X.; Hu, X. Optimization of pectin extraction assisted by microwave from apple pomace using response surface methodology. *J. Food Eng.* **2007**, *78*, 693–700. [CrossRef]

28. Rezzoug, S.A.; Boutekedjiret, C.; Allaf, K. Optimization of operating conditions of rosemary essential oil extraction by a fast controlled pressure drop process using response surface methodology. *J. Food Eng.* **2005**, *71*, 9–17. [CrossRef]

29. Kasankala, L.M.; Xue, Y.; Weilong, Y.; Hong, S.D.; He, Q. Optimization of gelatine extraction from grass carp (*Catenopharyngodon idella*) fish skin by response surface methodology. *Bioresour. Technol.* **2007**, *98*, 3338–3343. [CrossRef] [PubMed]

30. Rostagno, M.A.; Prado, J.M. *Natural Product Extraction: Principles and Applications*; Royal Society of Chemistry: Cambridge, UK, 2013.

Article

Polyphenols from Red Vine Leaves Using Alternative Processing Techniques

Simone Bachtler and Hans-Jörg Bart *

Chair of Separation Science and Technology, TU Kaiserslautern, 67663 Kaiserslautern, Germany;
simone.bachtler@mv.uni-kl.de
* Correspondence: bart@mv.uni-kl.de; Tel.: +49-(0)631-205-2414; Fax: +49-(0)631-205-2119

Received: 31 October 2018; Accepted: 10 December 2018; Published: 12 December 2018

Abstract: The extraction kinetics of polyphenols, which are leached from red vine leaves, are studied and evaluated using a laboratory robot and nonconventional processing techniques such as ultrasonic (US)-, microwave (MW)-, and pulsed electric field (PEF)-assisted extraction processes. The robotic high-throughput screening reveals optimal extraction conditions at a pH value of 2.5, a temperature of 56 °C, and a solvent mixture of methanol:water:HCl of 50:49:1 $v/v/v$. Nonconventional processing techniques, such as MW- and US-assisted extraction, have the fastest kinetics and produce the highest polyphenol yield. The non-conventional techniques yield is 2.29 g/L (MW) resp. 2.47 g/L (US) for particles that range in size from 450 to 2000 µm and 2.20 g/L (MW) resp. 2.05 g/L (US) for particles that range from 2000 to 4000 µm. PEF has the lowest yield of polyphenols with 0.94 g/L (450–2000 µm), resp. 0.64 g/L (2000–4000 µm) in comparison to 1.82 g/L (2000 to 4000 µm) in a standard stirred vessel (50 °C). When undried red vine leaves (2000 to 4000 µm) are used the total phenol content is 1.44 g/L with PEF.

Keywords: red vine leaves; polyphenols; microwaves; ultrasonic waves; pulsed electric fields; laboratory robot; extraction

---

1. Introduction

Extracts from vitis vinifera (red vine leaves) are used in herbal medicine and can help to relieve symptoms related to chronic venous insufficiency, such as swollen legs (edema), varicose veins, a feeling of heaviness, pain, tiredness, itching, and tension [1,2]. Red vine leaf extract primarily consists of secondary plant substances with polyphenols as the most important ones, e.g., flavonols, anthocyanins, and resveratrol [3]. Polyphenols, which have the greatest potential as pharmaceutical drugs, are recovered from red vine leaves by leaching using appropriate solvents [2], like acidified water and methanol due to polarity and stability reasons [4]. In general, the solid–liquid extraction process is limited by the low yield of polyphenols and slow extraction kinetics, which is caused by the morphology of the plant material [5]. For example, 1 kg red vine leaves yield about 70 g polyphenols depending on the strain of vitis vinifera, climate and location where the strain is grown as well as the timing of the harvest.

The cell morphology of red vine leaves mainly influences the thermodynamic partition equilibrium in the solid–liquid extraction process as the localization of polyphenols is in the vacuoles surrounded by robust and stable cell membranes [5,6]. The diffusion and mass transfer of polyphenols can be enhanced and accelerated by alternative methods of natural plant extraction and process intensification that promote cell membrane disruption. The energy to disrupt plant cell membranes is provided by ultrasonic waves (US) [7–9], microwaves (MW) [10–12], or by the use of pulsed electric fields (PEF) [13–17]. US-assisted extraction generates turbulences and thermal effects promoting extraction, as well as production and growth of bubbles inside liquids causing cavitation leading to structural attacks [18]. Cavitation bubbles can implode near a solid surface as a microjet [19,20] breaking up plant cell membranes [21–23]. An alternative to improve efficiency of natural plant extraction processes is by applying MW [24–26]. The MW radiation penetrates the target plant material and interacts with polar molecules through ionic conduction and dipole rotation [27] to generate heat. Adsorption and penetration depth, which are dependent on the dielectric constant and the dielectric loss of the material [28], are determined by the frequency of the MW [29]. The MW radiation increases the local temperature leading to an increase of the internal pressure of plant cells. The plant cells are primarily comprised of a vacuole filled with intracellular water and secondary metabolites that consequently rupture under pressure [30] and promote kinetics [31]. The PEF-assisted technique is based on the electroporation phenomenon of the cell membranes, when a potential difference arises across a membrane [32,33]. During electroporation, molecular orientation takes place where the polar molecules align themselves with the electric field and migrate to the membrane induced by the electric field [34]. The electrocompression starts to rupture the membrane and creates pores [35]. This can result in a temporary (reversible) or permanent (irreversible) loss of membrane permeability [36,37]. The extent of the loss in permeability and the pore formation depends on the induction of a critical electric field strength and cell size in a range of 1–2 kV/cm for a plant cell size of 40 to 200 μm [38].

In general, a typical extraction setup consists of a batch stirred vessel with temperature control and has been widely applied in the industry [39]. Even though the set-up is ubiquitous, the optimum extraction conditions which maximizes solid-liquid extraction with minimal energy input and costs has not identified [40,41]. For identifying optimal conditions of a solid–liquid extraction, a laboratory robot provides a systematic and highly reproducible process development [42–44]. Temperature, pH value, and solvent composition influence not only extraction kinetics and pseudostationary equilibrium but also solubility and stability of the extracted secondary metabolites [45,46]. A robot workstation allows high-throughput experiments and saves time by permitting unattended overnight operation [47]. Additionally, solid–liquid extraction processing plants require an appropriate design reflecting the unique characteristics of any plant material, as the solute can be in root, leaf, fruit, etc. Thus, effective diffusivity is an important transport property to consider when designing mass transfer equipment and increasing the scale of the process [48]. The most widely accepted models used to describe the extraction kinetics are: Fick's law of diffusion [49–52], the modified chemical kinetic equations [53–55], and the two-parametric empirical equations [56,57].

In this study, a custom-built laboratory robot is used to screen for the optimal conditions of a natural plant extraction process as temperature, pH value, and solvent composition are varied. For comparison, a standard stirred vessel experiment is used with alternative techniques, such as ultrasonification, microwaves or pulsed electric fields.

2. Materials and Methods

2.1. Preparation of Red Vine Leaves and Chemicals

Red vine leaves (*Vitis vinifera*, DAKAPO GN7225-8 Deckrot x Portugieser Börner) were collected on 3 October 2014 in Geisenheim (RP), Germany, and dried at 75 °C for 48 h (UT6120, Heraeus Holding GmbH, Hanau, Germany). After drying, the red vine leaves were manually ground in a mortar using a pestle. The bruised red vine leaf powder was sieved into 3 fractions by riddle screens (Analysette 3 PRO, Frisch GmbH, Idar-Oberstein, Germany) with 200 μm, 450 μm, 2000 μm, and 4000 μm mesh sizes. Furthermore, the bulk densities ρ_s were determined by filling a 10 mL measuring cylinder (Brand GmbH & Co KG, Wertheim, Germany) with 5 mL the red vine leaves and the filled measuring cylinder was weighed using an analytical balance (1702, Sartorius AG, Göttingen, Germany). The particle size distribution is displayed in Figure 1 and further details are given in Table 1. For measurements with undried red vine leaves a part of the collection was stored in a freezer (GS26DN11, Siemens AG, München, Germany) at a temperature of −18 °C. After defrosting, the red vine leaves were cut into 2 to 4 mm pieces by a scalpel. To maintain comparability with the dried red vine leaves the moisture content was calculated by weighing the undried red vine leaves and reweighing these red vine leaves after drying. The loss of water averaged $72.7 \pm 3.7\%$ in the course of 5 experiments.

The solvents were deionized water (0.01 µS/cm) mixed with hydrochloric acid (35–38%, CHEMSOLUTE®, Th. Geyer GmbH & Co. KG, Renningen, Germany) at pH values of 1.21, 1.53, 2.00, 2.50, and 3.00 and pure methanol ($\geq$99.9%, Sigma-Aldrich, St. Louis, MO, USA). The pH value was measured with a pH meter (pH 526, WTW, Weilheim, Germany).

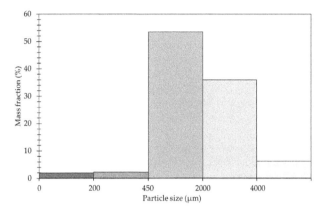

Figure 1. Particle size distribution of dried red vine leaves.

2.2. Folin–Ciocalteu Assay

Concentration measurement was done by UV/Vis spectrometry (UV-mini 1240, Shimadzu Corporation, Kyōto, Japan). The Folin–Ciocalteu assay was performed as described in detail in [58] using Folin–Ciocalteu reagent (Merck KGaA, Darmstadt, Germany) and Na_2CO_3 (Bernd Kraft GmbH, Duisburg, Germany).

2.3. Extraction Apparatus

Each extraction measurement was repeated 3 to 5 times and the ratio of red vine leaves to extractant was set to 40 g/L. In detail, the weighed portions m_s and the volumes of the solvents V_l are given in Table 1. In order to determine the optimal extraction conditions and partition equilibria, a custom-built laboratory robot (Lissy 4G200, Zinsser Analytic GmbH, Eschborn, Germany) and red vine leaves with particle size of 200 to 450 µm were used. In 8 vials red vine leave powder is suspended and shaken in time intervals of t = 1, 5, 10, 15, 30, 60, 90, and 120 min. The regulated thermostat temperatures of 25 °C, 35 °C, 45 °C, 55 °C, 60 °C, and 65 °C yielded temperatures in the extraction vials of 23.0 °C, 34.0 °C, 43.0 °C, 51.0 °C, 56.0 °C, and 60.5 °C, respectively. After agitation with a shaking rate of v = 400 rpm samples were taken and filtered using a mesh size of 1 µm (7700-9905, Whatman plc, Little Chalfont, UK). Details of the laboratory robot and its handling is described in detail in [42].

For comparison an 1 L jacketed tank held at 50 °C was used. The 1 L jacketed tank is equipped with a propeller mixer adjusted to 39 rpm and a metal mesh cage that retains the dried red vine leaves (2000 to 4000 µm) when using a solvent volume of 250 mL.

2.4. Alternative Extraction Techniques

For the alternative extraction techniques, red vine leaves with particle sizes of 450 to 2000 µm (size small, SS) and 2000 to 4000 µm (size large, SL) were used. Additionally, the temperature of the extraction slurry was measured with a PT100 probe when a sample was removed for the UV/Vis analysis (UV-mini 1240, Shimadzu Corporation, Kyōto, Japan).

The microwave assisted extraction (MW) was performed in a microwave oven (MW 4000, Landgraf Laborsysteme HLL GmbH, Langenhagen, Germany) using a 50 mL vessel containing a stirring bar and an immersed PT100 probe and operates at $P = 800$ W (100%). For temperature control of the extraction batch vessel (50 °C or 60 °C) the immersed PT100 controller is connected to a two-level controller, which regulates the power of the microwave.

The ultrasonic-assisted extraction (US) was executed using an ultrasonic probe (Bioblock Scientific Vibra Cell VC 750, Standard Probe $\frac{1}{2}$", Thermo Fisher Scientific Inc., Waltham, MA, USA) at a frequency of 20 kHz. The ultrasonic probe was dipped in a stirred 150 mL jacketed tank and the maximum amplitude (114 µm) was reduced to 30% (34.2 µm) or 40% (45.2 µm). During 120 min of application the US probe generates $W = 115.66$ kJ and $W = 198.24$ kJ of energy at 30% and at 40% of the maximal amplitude, respectively. With $P = \frac{W}{t}$ the energy input is correlated to an effective power of $P = 16.1$ W, respectively 27.5 W.

For the pulsed electric field assisted extraction (PEF) the setup consists of a high voltage generator (610C, Trek Inc., Lockport, NY, USA), an impulse generator (8035, Hameg Instruments GmbH, Mainhausen, Germany), a Schmitt trigger circuit, a high voltage switch, an oscilloscope (D1010, Siemens AG, München, Germany), and 2 plate electrodes (1.4301). Plate electrodes with a separation distance d of 0.42 cm and a surface A of 6 cm^2 were located in a 20 mL mixed glass beaker. The pulsed electric field setup generates monopolar exponential pulses for a duration of $t_i = 1$ ms with $\Delta t = 600$ ms intervals between pulses. The voltage was set to $U = 1.4$ kV or $U = 0.7$ kV and using $E = \frac{U}{d}$ the setup generates an electric field strength of 3.33 kV/cm or 1.67 kV/cm, respectively. The electrical power is given by $P_{el} = U \times I$ where the current I is calculated by Ohm's law and the electric resistance R is defined by $R = \frac{d}{\sigma_i A}$. The conductivity σ_i was measured after 120 min application time with a conductivity electrode (Seven2Go^{TM} S3, Mettler-Toledo, Columbus, OH, USA) giving 1.030 mS/cm for $U = 1.4$ kV, resp. 0.960 mS/cm for $U = 0.7$ kV. The resulting effective power is $P_{el} = 28.84$ kW, respectively $P_{el} = 6.14$ kW. Using undried red vine leaves the PEF assisted extraction process was executed with a voltage of $U = 1.4$ kV, a conductivity of $\sigma_i = 1.425$ mS/cm and an electric power of $P_{el} = 39.90$ kW.

2.5. Mass Transfer

Fick's law is used to describe the mass transfer and several simplifications have been made to enable the comparison of different techniques. The diffusion of the polyphenols is not hindered by other components and there is only one pseudo-solute (gallic acid [59,60]) diffusing. It is assumed that the dispersed solid material is an assembly of spherical particles of the same size with radius r and bulk density ρ_s [61]. The volume V_s of the red vine leaves is then related to their surface area A_s and to their total mass m_s:

$$V_s = A_s \times r/3 = m_s/\rho_s \tag{1}$$

A decrease in the thickness of the diffusion layer, which surrounds each particle, as stirring increases, is neglected. Thus, the flux J is equal to the amount of polyphenols c entering the bulk solution V_l in unit time t. The mass transfer from the beginning until equilibrium is analyzed from experimental data. Thus, the flux J is given by

$$J = A_s D_{eff} \Delta c_s / r = d(c \times V_l)/dt \tag{2}$$

where D_{eff} is the diffusion coefficient, V_l is the volume of the bulk, and Δc_s is the difference of the polyphenol concentrations at the center and at the periphery of a given particle, considering the m_l to m_s ratio:

$$c_s = \frac{m_l}{m_s} \times c_\infty \tag{3}$$

where c_∞ is the equilibrium concentration and m_l the mass of the bulk liquid resp. of m_s of the solid. With Equation (3), when knowing both masses and the equilibrium concentration, the initial (pseudo)polyphenol content in the particle can be calculated. For calculating the effective diffusion coefficient D_{eff} according to Equation (2), all data are given in Table 1. The mass of the bulk m_l is given by

$$m_l = \omega_{water} \times m_{l,water} + \omega_{meOH} \times m_{l,meOH} \tag{4}$$

where ω_{water} and ω_{meOH} are the mass percentage of water and methanol, neglecting the amount of HCl. The amounts of water $m_{l,water}$ and methanol $m_{l,meOH}$ are defined by the density ρ_l [62] and the volume V_l.

Table 1. Red vine leaves properties and extraction conditions.

Particle Size (μm)	r (μm)	ρ_s (g/mL)	m_s (g)	A_s (dm²)	V_l (mL)	T (°C)	$\rho_{l,water}$ (kg/m³)	$m_{l,water}$ (g)	$\rho_{l,methanol}$ (kg/m³)	Mixing Ratio [a] (% v/v)	m_l (g)
						51.0	987.58	2.47			
						56.0	985.21	2.46			
						60.5	982.95	2.46			
						56.0	985.21		752.16	20:80	2.35
										50:50	2.18
										80:20	2.00
MW	450–2000	612.5	0.19	1.09	2.82	25.0	50	988.05	24.7		
	2000–4000	1500	0.12	1.04	1.74	25.0			24.7		
US	450–2000	612.5	0.19	3.96	10.20	100	50	988.05	98.8		
	2000–4000	1500	0.12	4.03	6.71	100			98.8		
PEF	450–2000	612.5	0.19	0.80	2.07	20.0	35	994.04	19.9		
	2000–4000	1500	0.12	0.80	1.34	20.0			19.9		
	undried	1500	0.37	2.95	1.57	20.0	35	994.04	19.9		
batch	450–2000	612.5	0.19	10.0	25.79	250	25	997.69	249.4		
	2000–4000	1500	0.12	10.0	16.68	250			249.4		

[a] mixing ratio water to methanol.

3. Results and Discussion

3.1. Laboratory Robot

The laboratory robot high throughput system was used for robust and stable screening for a particle size of 200 to 450 μm (SS). Single parameter variation in respect to temperature and the composition of the solvent was performed and results of solute release are shown in Figure 2.

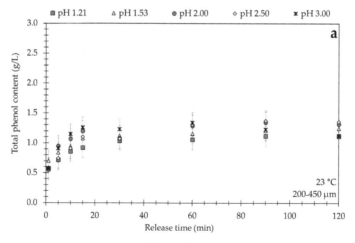

Figure 2. *Cont.*

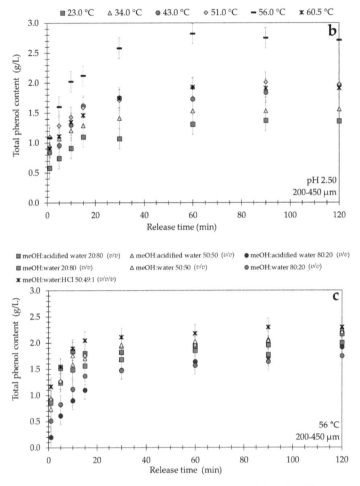

Figure 2. Extraction kinetics using laboratory robot by variation of pH value (**a**), temperature (**b**), and solvent (**c**) with size small (SS) plant material.

The study of Fossen et al. [63] revealed that pH values between 1.0 and 3.0 are most effective for the stability of anthocyanins, which are, like the flavonoids, a subgroup of polyphenols. Based on these results at 23 °C the pH values of 1.21, 1.53, 2.00, 2.50, and 3.00 were selected. Higher pH values were not applied due to the instability of polyphenols at higher pH values. As seen in Figure 2a, all leaching curves are very similar and acidity does not influence the extraction process significantly. The pseudo-equilibrium concentration is between $c_\infty = 1.12$ g/L and $c_\infty = 1.36$ g/L as shown in Table 2. The effective diffusion coefficient D_{eff} according to Equation (2) ranges from 0.68×10^{-12} m²/s to 1.39×10^{-12} m²/s, as the highest value of the effective diffusion coefficient was observed at a pH $= 3.00$. However, after 60 min the total polyphenol content gradually decreases from $c = 1.34$ g/L to $c_\infty = 1.13$ g/L. This slight decrease indicates that the polyphenols at this condition are becoming unstable and are beginning to degrade. Türker et al. [64] investigated the extraction of anthocyanins from carrots and confirmed the lower stability at a pH value of 3.00 and higher stability at a pH value of 2.00. Due to these results and given the conditions producing related to the highest extraction yield of $c_\infty = 1.36$ g/L a pH value of 2.50 was chosen for further measurements.

Table 2. Release data at different pH values.

pH	T (°C)	Extractant	c (g/L)	t (min)	c_∞ (g/L)	D_{eff} (10^{-12} m^2/s)	c_S (% w/w)
1.21	23.0	acidified water (HCl)	1.12	90	1.12	0.73	12.7
1.53			1.25	120	1.25	0.68	14.2
2.00			1.35	90	1.32	1.06	15.0
2.50			1.37	90	1.36	0.88	15.4
3.00			1.34	60	1.13	1.39	12.8

In contrast to pH value, a varying the extraction temperature from 23.0 °C to 60.5 °C most significantly effects the yield of polyphenols as shown in Figure 2b. According to Table 3, the highest concentration of polyphenols of $c_\infty = 2.71$ g/L was found at a temperature of 56 °C after 120 min. extraction time with acidified water at a pH = 2.50 with temperature steadily increased from 23.0 °C to 56.0 °C. Generally, it can be concluded that increasing temperature enhances the extraction efficiency, a conclusion supported by the study of Franco et al. [65]. They investigated the extraction of polyphenols from grape marc using water at temperatures of 25 °C and 50 °C and found that at 50 °C the yield is 80% higher than at 25 °C after 90 min of extraction, what is similar to our findings. Nevertheless, there is a temperature limit, which can be seen with the curve at $T = 60.5$ °C. At this highest temperature, degradation starts already immediately in the plant material leading to reduced yields.

Table 3. Release data at different temperatures.

pH	T (°C)	Extractant	c (g/L)	t (min)	c_∞ (g/L)	D_{eff} (10^{-12} m^2/s)	c_S (% w/w)
2.50	23.0	acidified water (HCl)	1.37	90	1.36	0.88	15.4
	34.0		1.56	120	1.56	0.51	17.6
	43.0		1.96	120	1.96	0.95	22.1
	51.0		2.01	90	1.97	0.57	22.1
	56.0		2.82	60	2.71	0.90	30.3
	60.5		1.93	60	1.91	0.69	21.3

In Figure 2c various solvent combinations of methanol and deionized water, at different acidities, were applied because these solvent mixtures have proven to be efficient for extraction of polyphenols [66–69]. In that respect combinations of (v/v) methanol and deionized water of 20:80, 50:50, and 80:20; methanol and acidified water at a pH value of 2.50 with a (v/v) of 20:80, 50:50, and 80:20; and methanol:water:HCl with a (v/v/v) of 50:49:1 at 56.0 °C were applied and the data are given in Table 4. The highest total phenol content $c_\infty = 2.38$ g/L was produced by the combinations methanol: acidified water 50:50 (v/v) and methanol:water:HCl (50:49:1 v/v/v) directly followed by the combination methanol:water 50:50 with total phenol content $c_\infty = 2.33$ g/L. When admixing methanol with water, the pH value does not markedly influence the content of polyphenols similar to the screening results in Figure 2a. Generally, increasing the methanol:water ratio to 80:20 reduces the pseudo-equilibrium concentration of polyphenols and thus the extraction capacity. The extraction process at $T = 56.0$ °C, which is very close to the boiling point of methanol, requires a closed extraction vessel to avoid methanol loss due to evaporation. Furthermore, the pseudostationary equilibrium is reached very quickly for methanol:water 80:20 (v/v) and methanol:acidified water 80:20 (v/v), which is supported by the highest effective diffusion coefficients of $D_{eff} = 1.39 \times 10^{-12}$ m^2/s and $D_{eff} = 1.21 \times 10^{-12}$ m^2/s, respectively.

Table 4. Release data using different solvents.

pH	T (°C)	Extractant	Mixing Ratio (% v/v/v)	c (g/L)	t (min)	c_∞ (g/L)	D_{eff} (10^{-12} m²/s)	c_s (% w/w)
2.59	56.0	meOH:acidified water	20:80	2.21	240	2.21	0.97	23.6
2.80			50:50	2.39	180	2.38	0.85	23.5
3.16			80:20	2.09	240	2.09	1.21	19.0
6.37		meOH:water	20:80	2.32	180	2.24	0.75	23.9
6.50			50:50	2.33	180	2.33	1.19	23.1
~7.0			80:20	1.76	240	1.76	1.39	16.0
1.38		meOH:water:HCl	50:49:1	2.38	240	2.38	0.98	23.5

In summary, unlike temperature increases or methanol admixtures, variations in acidity do not influence the extraction kinetics. Here the extraction temperature of approximately 56.0 °C gives the best yield $c_\infty = 2.71$ g/L with acidified water and the combination methanol:water 80:20 (v/v) shows the highest effective diffusion coefficient $D_{eff} = 1.39 \times 10^{-12}$ m²/s similar to the results with acidified water at pH = 3.0. The study of Kähkönen et al. [70] confirms that hot water yields the highest polyphenol content and admixtures of organic solvents can be harmful as the extract composition may change [70]. Furthermore, the study of Ju et al. [71] shows a similar outcome to water acidified with HCl (pH = 2.30) and acidified methanol solution (pH = 2.40) indicating similar efficiency for extraction of anthocyanins from grape skin.

3.2. Nonconventional Processing Techniques

Based on the screening results the two different samples (SS and SL) were extracted in the microwave oven (MW) at 50 °C and 60 °C. Figure 3 (1 MW) depicts the extraction kinetics (the total phenol content on left axis) and measured temperature (right axis) during 120 min application time as full and dash lines. The results are in line with the laboratory robot results at 50 °C or 60 °C, and the short overshooting of the two-level controller (energy input of $P = 800$ W) gives no obvious performance loss.

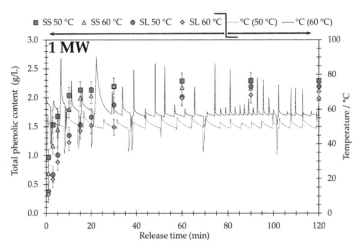

Figure 3. Extraction kinetics (left axis) and measured temperature curves (right axis) using microwaves (MW).

In comparison, the US probe with an amplitude of 30% gives a temperature around 50 °C whereas an amplitude of 40% raises the temperature to almost 60 °C, as depicted in Figure 4 (2 US). The slope of the measured temperature curves (full and dashed lines) follows the slope of the total phenol content curves. This indicates that only a portion of the cavitation bubbles break up the herbal cell membranes and the main energy of the compression waves heats up the extraction slurry and friction loss and limits the yield of polyphenols. It is apparent that changing the amplitude will not significantly improve the extraction.

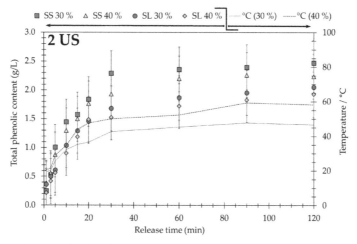

Figure 4. Extraction kinetics (left axis) and measured temperature curves (right axis) using ultrasonics (US).

In contrast to MW and US, the PEF-assisted technique (see Figure 5, 3 PEF) increases the temperature of the extraction slurry up to 35.0 °C for $U = 1.4$ kV and to 27.8 °C for $U = 0.7$ kV due to Joule heating, although the input of electrical power from $P = 6.14$ kW to $P = 28.84$ kW is very high. As can be seen, the increase of temperature is dependent on the intensity of the electric field and on the treatment time [72]. As to this, the application of PEF assisted processes in combination with mild heating presents a promising technique for benign extraction of thermal sensitive solutes. As mentioned, the temperature rise is not dramatic and the pseudo-equilibrium is reached after 60 min. Additionally, in accordance to the screening experiments (pH value, temperature, and solvent) of the laboratory robot, no degradation of polyphenols is observed during 120 min of extraction time.

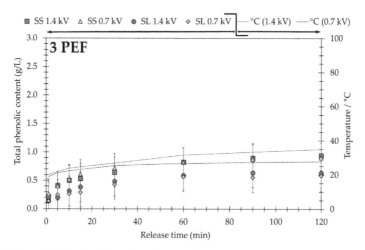

Figure 5. Extraction kinetics (left axis) and measured temperature curves (right axis) using pulsed electric field (PEF).

Generally, bigger particle size causes a lower yield due to longer diffusion paths and consequently a higher diffusion resistance [5,50]. The dependence of yield on particle size indicates that the diffusion of the solvent into the particle and the solvent–solute diffusion out of the particle are rate-determining steps of the process. Because of the dependence of the effective diffusion coefficient D_{eff} on particle size r, it is crucial to note that particle size is a decisive variable for process control.

3.3. Comparison of Nonconventional Processing Techniques

Although nonconventional processing techniques have different active principles, a comparison using the large red vine leaves (SL) is shown in Figure 6 and a conventional batch stirred vessel held at 50 °C is the reference. Generally, within 60 min extraction time the MW-, US-, or PEF-assisted technique achieved a higher yield of polyphenols than the standard extraction process. An exception is the PEF-assisted extraction process using dried red vine leaves. The lower effectiveness of PEF assisted extraction technique can be understood in context of the properties of the dried red vine leaves. It is harder to overcome the transmembrane potential and create pores, which is confirmed by the results of PEF with dried plant material and undried plant material. After harvesting and drying, the red vine leaves not only lose their moisture, especially the intracellular fluid, but also the structural integrity of the cell membrane pores is possibly damaged, which limits the effectiveness of PEF. In contrast, PEF assisted extraction of fresh red vine leaves leads to a total phenol content to $c_\infty = 1.44$ g/L (see Table 5). However, MW- and US-assisted extraction techniques are more effective [73] and temperature changes resulting from the energy input is the crucial factor for increasing yield. The MW-assisted extraction process achieves the highest total phenol content followed closely by the US-assisted extraction technique.

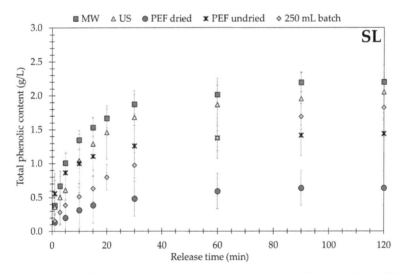

Figure 6. Extraction kinetics using alternative processing techniques and large sample size (SL).

Considering the effective diffusion coefficient, the PEF assisted technique that uses undried red vine leaves attains the pseudo-equilibrium most rapidly. In contrast to this, the effective diffusion coefficients of the other processing techniques are much lower as can be seen from Table 5. With $D_{eff} = 26.6 \times 10^{-12}$ m^2/s the standard jacketed tank has the lowest value and after 120 min release time the pseudo-equilibrium is still not reached (see Figure 6).

Table 5. Comparison of techniques.

	Particle Size (μm)	c_∞ (g/L)	D_{eff} $(10^{-12} m^2/s)$	c_s (% w/w)
microwave	2000–4000	2.20	55.1	43.3
ultrasonic probe		2.05	50.7	41.9
pulsed electric field	dried	0.64	43.1	13.2
pulsed electric field	undried	1.44	121	2.6
250 mL batch		1.82	26.6	37.9

4. Conclusions

The influence of temperature and solvent composition on extraction kinetics and saturation and degradation limits is screened using a fully automated laboratory robot for the optimization of solid–liquid extraction when leaching polyphenols from red vine leaves. Gallic acid was considered to be the representative pseudo-solute. The results generated by the laboratory robot show that varying the acidity of extracting agent does not influence the polyphenols yield and extraction kinetics. However, an increasing temperature markedly enhances the extraction yield and saturation concentration, but does not significantly improve extraction kinetics. An upper limit is given as polyphenols are thermally sensitive and the extraction efficiency is reduced at temperatures higher than 60 °C. When investigating different amounts of methanol as a modifier at an extraction temperature of 56 °C, a mixture of methanol:water 50:50 (v/v) independent of the pH value gives fast kinetics and the highest yield. However, methanol/water solutions give nearly results as acidified methanol/water solutions, and best results were when using only acidified water. In conclusion, the laboratory robot allows systematic and highly reproducible screenings of process conditions. Furthermore, the use of the laboratory robot allows massive time savings during screening with parallel and unattended overnight work.

With nonconventional processing techniques, like microwave, ultrasonic, and pulsed electric field, smaller particle size positively influences the extraction process due to a shorter diffusion path and higher surface area per volume. As a result, an appropriate sample preparation and combination is recommended with respect to industrial application with either filtering limits after maceration or a limiting pressure loss with percolation.

Generally, the microwave-assisted extraction process followed by the ultrasonic-assisted extraction process gives the highest yield of polyphenols at approximately 50 °C. PEF are less effective than MW or US assisted extraction in comparison to conventional batch extraction. Interestingly, US when combined with undried plant material presents a promising technique for benign extraction of thermal sensitive solutes. Finally, the best industrial extraction procedure for leaching polyphenols from red vine leaves uses a batch reactor with implemented magnetrons to generate microwaves and quickly heat suspended plant material.

Author Contributions: S.B. conceived and designed the experiments; S.B. performed the experiments and analyzed the data; H.-J.B. contributed reagents, materials and analysis tools; S.B. and H.-J.B. wrote the paper.

Funding: This research received no external funding.

Acknowledgments: We wish to thank Boehringer Ingelheim Pharma GmbH & Co.KG (H.J. Hagels) for helping with analytics and supplying HPLC standards.

Conflicts of Interest: The authors declare no conflict of interest.

Nomenclature

A_s	Surface area of red vine leaves (dm^2)
c	Polyphenol concentration in the bulk (g/L)
c_s	Polyphenol concentration considering the m_l to m_s ratio (% w/w)
c_∞	Polyphenol concentration at pseudo-equilibrium (g/L)
D_{eff}	Effective diffusion coefficient (10^{-12} m^2/s)
E	Electric field strength (kV/cm)
I	Current (A)
J	Diffusive mass flux (g/min)
m_l	Weight of the bulk (g)
m_s	Weight of the red vine leaves (g)
$m_{l,meOH}$	Weight of the methanol bulk (g)
$m_{l,water}$	Weight of the water bulk (g)
P	Power (W)
P_{el}	Electric power (W)
R	Resistance (Ω)
r	Particle radius (μm)
ρ_s	Bulk density (g/mL)
$\rho_{l,water}$	Density of water (kg/m^3)
$\rho_{l,water}$	Density of methanol (kg/m^3)
σ_i	Conductivity (mS/cm)
t	Release time (min)
t_∞	Pseudo-equilibrium time (min)
T	Extraction temperature ($^\circ$C)
U	Voltage (kV)
V_l	Bulk volume (L)
V_s	Volume of the red vine leaves (m^3)
W	Energy (kJ)
ω_{meOH}	Mass fraction of water
ω_{water}	Mass fraction of methanol

References

1. Schneider, E. Rotes Weinlaub—Geschichte der Verwendung in der Medizin. *Schweiz. Z. GanzheitsMed.* **2009**, *8*, 333–339. [CrossRef]
2. Esperester, A.; Frey, H.W.; Vix, J.-M. Method for Treatment of Chronic Venous Insufficiencies Using an Extract of Red Vine Leaves. U.S. Patent US6485727B1, 26 November 2002.
3. Schneider, E. Rotes Weinlaub—Eine venenwirksame Arzneidroge. *Dtsch. Apoth. Ztg.* **2007**, *147*, 40–47.
4. Chethan, S.; Malleshi, N.G. Finger millet polyphenols: Optimization of extraction and the effect of pH on their stability. *Food Chem.* **2007**, *105*, 862–870. [CrossRef]
5. Schneider, F.H. *Extraktive Trennung Fest/Flüssig: Untersuchungen Über die Feinstruktur Vegetabiler Feststoffe und Ihren Einfluß auf das Extraktionsverhalten*; Forschungsberichte des Landes Nordrhein-Westfalen; Springer: Essen, Germany, 1980.
6. Cheynier, V. Polyphenols in foods are more complex than often thought. *Am. J. Clin. Nutr.* **2005**, *81*, 223S–229S. [CrossRef]
7. Esclapez, M.D.; García-Pérez, J.V.; Mulet, A.; Cárcel, J.A. Ultrasound-Assisted Extraction of Natural Products. *Food Eng. Rev.* **2011**, *3*, 108–120. [CrossRef]
8. Luque-García, J.L.; de Castro, M.D.L. Ultrasound: A powerful tool for leaching. *Trends Anal. Chem.* **2003**, *22*, 41–47. [CrossRef]
9. Shirsath, S.R.; Sonawane, S.H.; Gogate, P.R. Intensification of extraction of natural products using ultrasonic irradiations—A review of current status. *Chem. Eng. Process.* **2012**, *53*, 10–23. [CrossRef]
10. Chan, C.-H.; Yusoff, R.; Ngoh, G.-C.; Kung, F.W.-L. Microwave-assisted extractions of active ingredients from plants. *J. Chromatogr. A* **2011**, *1218*, 6213–6225. [CrossRef]

11. Filly, A.; Fernandez, X.; Minuti, M.; Visinoni, F.; Cravotto, G.; Chemat, F. Solvent-free microwave extraction of essential oil from aromatic herbs: From laboratory to pilot and industrial scale. *Food Chem.* **2014**, *150*, 193–198. [CrossRef]

12. Zhang, H.-F.; Yang, X.-H.; Wang, Y. Microwave assisted extraction of secondary metabolites from plants: Current status and future directions. *Trends Food Sci. Technol.* **2011**, *22*, 672–688. [CrossRef]

13. Brodelius, P.E.; Funk, C.; Shillito, R.D. Permeabilization of cultivated plant cells by electroporation for release of intracellularly stored secondary products. *Plant Cell Rep.* **1988**, *7*, 186–188. [CrossRef]

14. Bouzrara, H.; Vorobiev, E. Solid–liquid expression of cellular materials enhanced by pulsed electric field. *Chem. Eng. Process.* **2003**, *42*, 249–257. [CrossRef]

15. Corrales, M.; Toepfl, S.; Butz, P.; Knorr, D.; Tauscher, B. Extraction of anthocyanins from grape by-products assisted by ultrasonics, high hydrostatic pressure or pulsed electric fields: A comparison. *Innov. Food Sci. Emerg. Technol.* **2008**, *9*, 85–91. [CrossRef]

16. Loginova, K.V.; Lebovka, N.I.; Vorobiev, E. Pulsed electric field assisted aqueous extraction of colorants from red beet. *J. Food Eng.* **2011**, *106*, 127–133. [CrossRef]

17. de Oliveira, C.F.; Giordani, D.; Gurak, P.D.; Cladera-Olivera, F.; Marczak, L.D.F. Extraction of pectin from passion fruit peel using moderate electric field and conventional heating extraction methods. *Innov. Food Sci. Emerg. Technol.* **2015**, *29*, 201–208. [CrossRef]

18. Chemat, F.; Rombaut, N.; Sicaire, A.-G.; Meullemiestre, A.; Fabiano-Tixier, A.-S.; Abert-Vian, M. Ultrasound assisted extraction of food and natural products. Mechanisms, techniques, combinations, protocols and applications. A review. *Ultrason. Sonochem.* **2017**, *34*, 540–560. [CrossRef]

19. Belova, V.; Gorin, D.A.; Shchukin, D.G.; Möhwald, H. Selektive Ultraschall-Kavitation an strukturierten hydrophoben Oberflächen. *Angew. Chem.* **2010**, *122*, 7285–7289. [CrossRef]

20. Toma, M.; Vinatoru, M.; Paniwnyk, L.; Mason, T.J. Investigation of the effects of ultrasound on vegetal tissues during solvent extraction. *Ultrason. Sonochem.* **2001**, *8*, 137–142. [CrossRef]

21. da Porto, C.; Porretto, E.; Decorti, D. Comparison of ultrasound-assisted extraction with conventional extraction methods of oil and polyphenols from grape (*Vitis vinifera* L.) seeds. *Ultrason. Sonochem.* **2013**, *20*, 1076–1080. [CrossRef]

22. Khan, M.K.; Abert-Vian, M.; Fabiano-Tixier, A.-S.; Dangles, O.; Chemat, F. Ultrasound-assisted extraction of polyphenols (flavanone glycosides) from orange (*Citrus sinensis* L.) peel. *Food Chem.* **2010**, *119*, 851–858. [CrossRef]

23. Pingret, D.; Fabiano-Tixier, A.-S.; le Bourvellec, C.; Renard, C.M.G.C.; Chemat, F. Lab and pilot-scale ultrasound-assisted water extraction of polyphenols from apple pomace. *J. Food Eng.* **2012**, *111*, 73–81. [CrossRef]

24. Pan, X.; Niu, G.; Liu, H. Microwave-assisted extraction of tea polyphenols and tea caffeine from green tea leaves. *Chem. Eng. Process.* **2003**, *42*, 129–133. [CrossRef]

25. Hao, J.-Y.; Han, W.; Huang, S.-D.; Xue, B.-Y.; Deng, X. Microwave-assisted extraction of artemisinin from *Artemisia annua* L. *Sep. Purif. Technol.* **2002**, *28*, 191–196. [CrossRef]

26. Proestos, C.; Komaitis, M. Application of microwave-assisted extraction to the fast extraction of plant phenolic compounds. *LWT Food Sci. Technol.* **2008**, *41*, 652–659. [CrossRef]

27. Destandau, E.; Michel, T.; Elfakir, C. Microwave-assisted Extraction. In *Natural Product Extraction: Principles and Applications*; Rostagno, M.A., Ed.; Royal Soc. of Chemistry: Cambridge, UK, 2013; pp. 113–156.

28. Alfaro, M.J.; Bélanger, J.M.R.; Padilla, F.C.; Paré, J.R.J. Influence of solvent, matrix dielectric properties, and applied power on the liquid-phase microwave-assisted processes (MAP^{TM}) extraction of ginger (Zingiber officinale). *Food Res. Int.* **2003**, *36*, 499–504. [CrossRef]

29. Routray, W.; Orsat, V. Microwave-Assisted Extraction of Flavonoids: A Review. *Food Bioprocess Technol.* **2012**, *5*, 409–424. [CrossRef]

30. Both, S.; Strube, J.; Cravotto, G. Mass Transfer Enhancement for Solid-Liquid Extractions. In *Green Extraction of Natural Products: Theory and Practice*; Chémat, F., Strube, J., Eds.; Wiley VCH: Weinheim, Germany, 2015; pp. 101–144.

31. Barba, F.J.; Galanakis, C.M.; Esteve, M.J.; Frigola, A.; Vorobiev, E. Potential use of pulsed electric technologies and ultrasounds to improve the recovery of high-added value compounds from blackberries. *J. Food Eng.* **2015**, *167*, 38–44. [CrossRef]

32. Weaver, J.C.; Chizmadzhev, Y.A. Theory of electroporation: A review. *Bioelectrochem. Bioenerg.* **1996**, *41*, 135–160. [CrossRef]

33. Vorobiev, E.; Lebovka, N. Pulsed-Electric-Fields-Induced Effects in Plant Tissues: Fundamental Aspects and Perspectives of Applications. In *Electrotechnologies for Extraction from Plant Foods and Biomaterials*; Vorobiev, E., Lebovka, N., Eds.; Springer: New York, NY, USA; London, UK, 2008; pp. 39–82.

34. Weaver, J.C. Electroporation of cells and tissues. *IEEE Trans. Plasma Sci.* **2000**, *28*, 24–33. [CrossRef]

35. Barnett, A.; Weaver, J.C. Electroporation: A unified, quantitative theory of reversible electrical breakdown and mechanical rupture in artificial planar bilayer membranes. *Bioelectrochem. Bioenerg.* **1991**, *25*, 163–182. [CrossRef]

36. Zimmermann, U.; Pilwat, G.; Beckers, F.; Riemann, F. Effects of External Electrical Fields on Cell Membranes. *Bioelectrochem. Bioenerg.* **1976**, *3*, 58–83. [CrossRef]

37. Morales-Cid, G.; Cárdenas, S.; Simonet, B.M.; Valcárcel, M. Sample treatments improved by electric fields. *Trends Anal. Chem.* **2010**, *29*, 158–165. [CrossRef]

38. Heinz, V.; Alvarez, I.; Angersbach, A.; Knorr, D. Preservation of liquid foods by high intensity pulsed electric fields—Basic concepts for process design. *Trends Food Sci. Technol.* **2001**, *12*, 103–111. [CrossRef]

39. Kassing, M.; Jenelten, U.; Schenk, J.; Strube, J. A New Approach for Process Development of Plant-Based Extraction Processes. *Chem. Eng. Technol.* **2010**, *33*, 377–387. [CrossRef]

40. Bart, H.-J.; Pilz, S. *Industrial Scale Natural Products Extraction*; Wiley-VCH: Weinheim, Germany, 2011.

41. Both, S.; Eggersglüß, J.; Lehnberger, A.; Schulz, T.; Schulze, T.; Strube, J. Optimizing Established Processes like Sugar Extraction from Sugar Beets—Design of Experiments versus Physicochemical Modeling. *Chem. Eng. Technol.* **2013**, *36*, 2125–2136. [CrossRef]

42. Bachtler, S.; Bart, H.-J. Extraction of Anthocyanins Using a Laboratory Robot and Innovative Extraction Technologies. *Chem. Eng. Technol.* **2016**, *39*, 1875–1883. [CrossRef]

43. Werner, A.; Blaschke, T.; von Harbou, E.; Hasse, H. Fully Automated Weighing of Liquid Substances with a Laboratory Robot. *Chem. Eng. Technol.* **2014**, *37*, 168–172. [CrossRef]

44. Both, S. *Systematische Verfahrensentwicklung für Pflanzlich Basierte Produkte im Regulatorischen Umfeld*; Shaker: Aachen, Germany, 2014.

45. Wang, L.; Weller, C.L. Recent advances in extraction of nutraceuticals from plants. *Trends Food Sci. Technol.* **2006**, *17*, 300–312. [CrossRef]

46. Bergs, D.; Merz, J.; Delp, A.; Joehnck, M.; Martin, G.; Schembecker, G. A Standard Procedure for the Selection of Solvents for Natural Plant Extraction in the Early Stages of Process Development. *Chem. Eng. Technol.* **2013**, *36*, 1739–1748. [CrossRef]

47. Chapman, T. A structured approach. *Nature* **2003**, *421*, 661–666. [CrossRef]

48. Chan, C.-H.; Yusoff, R.; Ngoh, G.-C. Modeling and kinetics study of conventional and assisted batch solvent extraction. *Chem. Eng. Res. Des.* **2014**, *92*, 1169–1186. [CrossRef]

49. Boussetta, N.; Vorobiev, E. Application of electrical treatments in alcoholic solvent for polyphenols extraction from grape seeds. *LWT Food Sci. Technol.* **2012**, *46*, 127–134. [CrossRef]

50. Herodez, S.S.; Hadolin, M.; Skerget, M.; Knez, Z. Solvent extraction study of antioxidants from Balm (*Melissa officinalis* L.) leaves. *Food Chem.* **2003**, *80*, 275–282. [CrossRef]

51. Hojnik, M.; Škerget, M.; Knez, Ž. Extraction of lutein from Marigold flower petals—Experimental kinetics and modelling. *LWT Food Sci. Technol.* **2008**, *41*, 2008–2016. [CrossRef]

52. Perez, E.E.; Carelli, A.A.; Crapiste, G.H. Temperature-dependent diffusion coefficient of oil from different sunflower seeds during extraction with hexane. *J. Food Eng.* **2011**, *105*, 180–185. [CrossRef]

53. Qu, W.; Pan, Z.; Ma, H. Extraction modeling and activities of antioxidants from pomegranate marc. *J. Food Eng.* **2010**, *99*, 16–23. [CrossRef]

54. Pan, G.; Yu, G.; Zhu, C.; Qiao, J. Optimization of ultrasound-assisted extraction (UAE) of flavonoids compounds (FC) from hawthorn seed (HS). *Ultrason. Sonochem.* **2012**, *19*, 486–490. [CrossRef]

55. Rakotondramasy-Rabesiaka, L.; Havet, J.-L.; Porte, C.; Fauduet, H. Solid–liquid extraction of protopine from *Fumaria officinalis* L.—Kinetic modelling of influential parameters. *Ind. Crops Prod.* **2009**, *29*, 516–523. [CrossRef]

56. Peleg, M. An Empirical Model for the Description of Moisture Sorption Curves. *J. Food Sci.* **1988**, *53*, 1216–1219. [CrossRef]

57. Velicković, D.T.; Milenović, D.M.; Ristić, M.S.; Veljković, V.B. Kinetics of ultrasonic extraction of extractive substances from garden (*Salvia officinalis* L.) and glutinous (*Salvia glutinosa* L.) sage. *Ultrason. Sonochem.* **2006**, *13*, 150–156. [CrossRef]
58. Ainsworth, E.A.; Gillespie, K.M. Estimation of total phenolic content and other oxidation substrates in plant tissues using Folin–Ciocalteu reagent. *Nat. Protoc.* **2007**, *2*, 875–877. [CrossRef]
59. Guerrero, M.S.; Torres, J.S.; Nuñez, M.J. Extraction of polyphenols from white distilled grape pomace: Optimization and modelling. *Bioresour. Technol.* **2008**, *99*, 1311–1318. [CrossRef]
60. Rakotondramasy-Rabesiaka, L.; Havet, J.-L.; Porte, C.; Fauduet, H. Estimation of effective diffusion and transfer rate during the protopine extraction process from *Fumaria officinalis* L. *Sep. Purif. Technol.* **2010**, *76*, 126–131. [CrossRef]
61. Spiro, M.; Selwood, R.M. The kinetics and mechanism of caffeine infusion from coffee: The effect of particle size. *J. Sci. Food Agric.* **1984**, *35*, 915–924. [CrossRef]
62. VDI-Gesellschaft Verfahrenstechnik und Chemieingenieurwesen (GVC). *VDI-Wärmeatlas*, 11th ed.; Springer: Berlin/Heidelberg, Germany, 2013.
63. Fossen, T.; Cabrita, L.; Andersen, O.M. Colour and stability of pure anthocyanins influenced by pH including the alkaline region. *Food Chem.* **1998**, *63*, 435–440. [CrossRef]
64. Türker, N.; Erdogdu, F. Effects of pH and temperature of extraction medium on effective diffusion coefficient of anthocynanin pigments of black carrot (*Daucus carota var.* L.). *J. Food Eng.* **2006**, *76*, 579–583. [CrossRef]
65. Franco, D.; Sineiro, J.; Rubilar, M.; Sánchez, M.; Jerez, M.; Pinelo, M.; Costoya, N.; Nunez, M.J. Polyphenols from plant materials: Extraction and antioxidant power. *Electron. J. Environ. Agric. Food Chem.* **2008**, *7*, 3210–3216.
66. Rødtjer, A.; Skibsted, L.H.; Andersen, M.L. Antioxidative and prooxidative effects of extracts made from cherry liqueur pomace. *Food Chem.* **2006**, *99*, 6–14. [CrossRef]
67. Kallithraka, S.; Garcia-Viguera, C.; Bridle, P.; Bakker, J. Survey of solvents for the extraction of grape seed phenolics. *Phytochem. Anal.* **1995**, *6*, 265–267. [CrossRef]
68. Lapornik, B.; Prošek, M.; Wondra, A.G. Comparison of extracts prepared from plant by-products using different solvents and extraction time. *J. Food Eng.* **2005**, *71*, 214–222. [CrossRef]
69. Revilla, E.; Ryan, J.-M.; Martín-Ortega, G. Comparison of Several Procedures Used for the Extraction of Anthocyanins from Red Grapes. *J. Agric. Food Chem.* **1998**, *46*, 4592–4597. [CrossRef]
70. Kähkönen, M.P.; Hopia, A.I.; Heinonen, M. Berry Phenolics and Their Antioxidant Activity. *J. Agric. Food Chem.* **2001**, *49*, 4076–4082. [CrossRef]
71. Ju, Z.Y.; Howard, L.R. Effects of solvent and temperature on pressurized liquid extraction of anthocyanins and total phenolics from dried red grape skin. *J. Agric. Food Chem.* **2003**, *51*, 5207–5213. [CrossRef]
72. Jäger, H. Process Performance Analysis of Pulsed Electric Field (PEF) Food Applications. Ph.D. Thesis, Technische Universität, Berlin, Germany, 2012.
73. Fang, X.; Wang, J.; Yu, X.; Zhang, G.; Zhao, J. Optimization of microwave-assisted extraction followed by RP-HPLC for the simultaneous determination of oleanolic acid and ursolic acid in the fruits of Chaenomeles sinensis. *J. Sep. Sci.* **2010**, *33*, 1147–1155. [CrossRef]

Article

Multiresponse Optimization of Ultrasonic-Assisted Extraction for Aurantii Fructus to Obtain High Yield of Antioxidant Flavonoids Using a Response Surface Methodology

Yingjie He [1,2,†], Yun Chen [1,2,†], Yiting Shi [1,2], Kanghong Zhao [2], Haiyan Tan [2], Jianguo Zeng [1], Qi Tang [1,2,*] and Hongqi Xie [1,2,*]

[1]   Hunan Key Laboratory of Traditional Chinese Veterinary Medicine, Hunan Agricultural University, Changsha 410128, China; yingjiehe272@163.com (Y.H.); m18250068565_1@163.com (Y.C.); erin643747964@163.com (Y.S.); zengjianguo@hunau.edu.cn (J.Z.)
[2]   Horticulture and Landscape College, Hunan Agricultural University, Changsha 410128, China; kanghongz@163.com (K.Z.); 15874589459@163.com (H.T.)
*   Correspondence: tangqi@hunau.edu.cn (Q.T.); xiehongqi@hunau.edu.cn (H.X.)
†   These authors contributed equally to this work.

Received: 6 November 2018; Accepted: 7 December 2018; Published: 10 December 2018

Abstract: Aurantii fructus (zhiqiao, ZQ) is a traditional Chinese medicine (TCM) and raw material of TCM healthcare food (TCM-HF), mainly focused on the regulation of gastrointestinal disorders and the abundant application of antioxidants. Pharmacological investigations of ZQ flavonoids have identified them as the main bioactive components in recent years, but little has been reported on the extraction processes of antioxidant flavonoids (AFs). The aim of this study was to establish an efficient ultrasonic-assisted extraction (UAE) method for the extraction of AFs from ZQ using a response surface methodology (RSM), analyze the composition of AFs, and develop a qualitative evaluation method for ZQ. Flavonoid yield and antioxidant ability were selected as the responses to optimize the extraction of AFs, and the multiple effects of independent variables were investigated. The optimized conditions for the extraction of AFs based on the Box-Behnken design (BBD) were as follows: ethanol concentration, 58%; extraction temperature, 70 °C; and extraction time, 17 min. The flavonoid yield and antioxidant activity reached 241.70 mg/g and 59.42%, respectively, which matched the predicted values. Furthermore, optimized UAE processes were first established for the efficient and fast extraction of AFs. Flavanones and polymethoxyflavonoids (PMFs) were identified as potential AFs using time-of-flight mass spectrometry. Meanwhile, the quality of ZQ was evaluated using the criteria importance through intercriteria correlation (CRITIC) method for the first time, and *Yuanjiang* ZQ was considered as an excellent raw material of TCM-HF.

Keywords: Aurantii fructus; antioxidant flavonoids; ultrasonic-assisted extraction; response surface methodology; criteria importance through intercriteria correlation method

---

1. Introduction

The importance of traditional Chinese medicine (TCM) has been accepted as a sustainable health treatment resource around the world. In recent years, the conception of TCM healthcare food (TCM-HF) has fast developed from a traditional treatment to dietotherapy [1]. Therefore, it has become increasingly important to explore active compounds from natural sources using essential extraction and isolation procedures in the application of pharmaceutic preparations, functional food components, dietary supplements, nutraceuticals, and food additives [2]. Research and development regarding TCM-HF mainly include formulae, quality standards and process procedures, and optimization of process procedures is essential. Moreover, antioxidant activity is one of the key indexes of TCM-HF and has been shown to eliminate or reduce the amount of free radicals and to decrease the incidence of diseases [3].

Aurantii fructus (zhiqiao, ZQ), a TCM and a raw material of TCM-HF, is harvested from the immature, green fruit of *Citrus aurantium* L., mainly focused on the treatment of gastrointestinal dysfunction, the improvement of qi stagnation, and the remission of chest pain in traditional therapies [4–6]. The secondary metabolites of ZQ include flavonoids, alkaloids, triterpenes, volatile oils, and coumarins [7–10]. Based on pharmacologic studies and clinical practice, flavonoids are considered as the main medicinal components with an enriched content and play an important role in pharmacological effects, such as anti-oxidation, anti-inflammation, the treatment of cardiovascular disease, and the promotion of gastrointestinal motility [11–14]. Although many studies have been carried out on the pharmacology and analytical chemistry of ZQ, there are few studies on the extraction technology of ZQ extract [15]. As a potential raw material of TCM-HF, it is important to develop an efficient and concise extraction procedure for the extraction of health-promoting compounds from ZQ. In pre-experiments for this study, we found that the flavonoid yield was positively correlated with antioxidant activity. According to the basic requirement of TCM-HF, extraction procedures for antioxidant flavonoids (AFs) from ZQ should be further studied [16].

In previous research, common extraction methods of ZQ flavonoids mainly included ultrasonic extraction [5,8], hot-water extraction [17,18], and reflux extraction [19]. Concerning the current study, there is no report on the ultrasonic-assisted hot-water extraction (UAE) method for the extraction of AFs from ZQ. In this study, UAE variables such as raw material concentration, sample size, extraction solvent, solvent concentration, extraction time, and extraction temperature were optimized using single-factor tests; among these, ethanol concentration, extraction temperature, and time were selected as the individual variables for the response surface methodology (RSM) by performing a three-level, three-variable Box-Behnken design (BBD) [20,21] to study the appropriate extraction conditions for AFs from ZQ. Then, we analyzed the main components of AFs from ZQ using liquid chromatography combined with quadrupole time-of-flight mass spectrometry (LC–Q–TOF–MS) [7] and evaluated the quality of ZQ from different habitats using the criteria importance through intercriteria correlation (CRITIC) method [22].

2. Materials and Methods

2.1. Materials, Chemicals, and Reagents

ZQ samples were collected from a series of raw materials of Hunan Province in China and identified by Prof. Qi Tang (Hunan Agricultural University). The fresh ZQs were continuously dried in 60 °C oven until a constant weight. The dried ZQ samples were milled with a grinder, sieved through a series of sieves, and stored in a desiccator at ordinary temperature (25 °C) until the tests. Standard substances (narirutin, naringin, eriocitrin, neoeriocitrin, poncirin, hesperidin, neohesperidin, nobiletin, and tangeretin) with high purities of over 98% were purchased from Yuan-ye Bio-Technology Co., Ltd. (Shanghai, China). Methanol, ethanol, acetone, ethyl acetate, ether, and petroleum ether were the analytical reagents (Sinopharm Chemical Reagent Co., Ltd., Shanghai, China). Acetonitrile and formic acid were of the chromatographic grade for the mass analysis (Sinopharm Chemical Reagent Co., Ltd., Shanghai, China).

2.2. Optimal Extraction of AFs from ZQ

An extractive procedure was optimized for the extraction of AFs; in short, 50 mg of each dried ZQ sample was added to 20 mL of 58% ethanol, and extracted for 17 min in a 70 °C water bath by use of a KM5200DV ultrasonic instrument with a constant power (200 W, 40 Hz; Kunshan Ultrasonic Instrument Co., Ltd., Kunshan, China).

2.3. Determination of Flavonoid Yield

The flavonoid yield of each extract was determined by Lay et al. [23], with few modifications. Each standard solution of naringin (200 μL) within a set concentration range (10, 40, 80, 120, 160, 200, 400 μg/mL) was added to 5.0 mL of 0.01 mol/L AlCl$_3$ solution (dissolved in methanol), respectively, incubated for 10 min in the dark at room temperature, and then measured at 310 nm on an 1800 UV spectrophotometer (Shimadzu Corp., Kyoto, Japan). A calibration curve was established: Y = 0.0009X − 0.0039, where Y was the absorbance (Abs), and X was the naringin concentration (μg/mL), R^2 = 0.9969.

An extract solution of 100 μL and 100 μL methanol solvent were mixed, and the same procedure was then repeated, as described above. The concentration of flavonoids was determined based on the calibration curve measured, and the flavonoid yield in the extract was calculated according to the naringin equivalent (mg of flavonoids/g of extract).

2.4. Analysis of Antioxidant Activity

The antioxidant activity of the ZQ extract was analyzed according to the free-radical scavenging activity and measured using the 1,1-diphenyl-2-picrylhydrazyl (DPPH) method. This method was performed as proposed by Lay et al. [23], with a minor modification. An extract solution of 3.0 mL was added to a tube and then mixed with 3.0 mL of 80 μg/mL DPPH/methanol solution. The mixture was incubated for 30 min in dark conditions at room temperature. After the reaction, the absorbance was recorded at a wavelength of 517 nm on an 1800 UV spectrophotometer. Methanol was used as a blank control. The antioxidant activity of the tested sample was expressed as the DPPH radical scavenging rate (SR).

The calculated equation was:

$$\% \text{ SR} = [(A_0 - A_1)/A_0] \times 100\%, \tag{1}$$

where A_0 is the blank control and A_1 is the absorbance sample.

2.5. Experimental RSM Design

Based on the single-factor tests, several independent variables which had a significant influence on flavonoid yield and antioxidant activity were selected as the factor variables and studied using the BBD of RSM.

2.6. Identification of AFs

The identification of AFs was conducted on an Agilent 1290 HPLC system (Agilent Technologies, Palo Alto, CA, USA), combined with an accurate-mass mass spectrometer of Agilent 6530 Q-TOF-MS (Agilent Technologies, Palo Alto, CA, USA). Chromatographic separation was carried out on an Agilent-ZORBAX SB-C18 column (250 mm × 4.6 mm, 5 μm, Agilent Technologies, Palo Alto, CA, USA), with a gradient elution (0–45 min, 10–90% acetonitrile). The other experimental conditions were consistent with our previous study [7].

2.7. Quality Evaluation of ZQ

Based on the optimal extraction conditions, the flavonoid yield and antioxidant activity of ZQ samples from 16 different habitats of Hunan Province were determined, and the criteria importance through intercriteria correlation (CRITIC) method was employed for the ZQ quality evaluation.

3. Results and Discussion

3.1. Selection of Optimization Factors

The solubility of AFs is affected by various variables. In this study, the ratio of solid/solvent was set to 50 mg/20 mL in the pre-test, which guaranteed an adequate dissolution of AFs, and a UAE with a consistent ultrasonic power of 200 W, 40 Hz was employed, which was mild for the molecular structure of the AFs. Furthermore, other independent variables were carefully screened using single-factor tests.

3.1.1. Selection of Organic Solvent for Extraction

Extraction solvents have a significant influence on extraction yield. The solubility of flavonoids is controlled by the polarity of the solvents used. Therefore, it is important to employ suitable solvents to ensure the optimal extraction of ZQ flavonoids. The ZQ flavonoids were extracted using different solvents from low polarity to high polarity, and their antioxidant activities were analyzed. The results showed that, compared to other solvents, the solubility of ZQ flavonoids in methanol and ethanol solution increased significantly, but there was no significant difference between them, and the antioxidant activity of ZQ extract in ethanol solution was better than in methanol (Figure 1A). In consideration of green environmental chemistry, which encourages low toxicity, environmental friendliness, and relative safety, ethanol solution was chosen as the extraction solution. Then, its concentration was tentatively set to 60% for further optimization (Figure 1E).

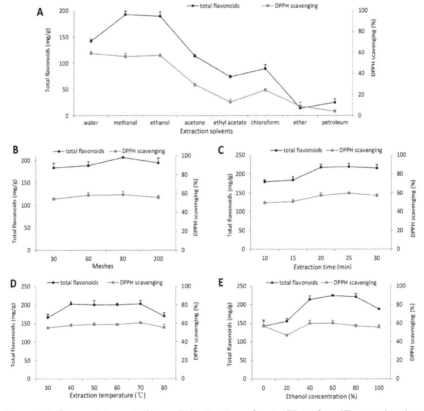

Figure 1. Influence of the main factors ((**A**) extraction solvents, (**B**) meshes, (**C**) extraction time, (**D**) extraction temperature, (**E**) ethanol concentration) on flavonoids and DPPH scavenging of Aurantii fructus.

3.1.2. Selection of Sieves

It was found that the sieve sizes were not very significant, being in the range of 30–200 meshes, but it was still clear that the flavonoid yield and antioxidant activity obtained from 80 meshes were suitable for ZQ extraction (Figure 1B).

3.1.3. Selection of Extraction Time

The effect of different extraction times on the flavonoid yield and antioxidant activity was studied. The results showed that both indexes first increased, and then decreased with longer extraction times (Figure 1C). An extraction time at 20 min was selected for further extraction optimization.

3.1.4. Selection of Extraction Temperature

Temperature had a great influence on flavonoid yield and antioxidant activity, but there was not a very significant difference in the range of 40–70 °C. As shown in Figure 1D, the composition of ZQ was relatively stable in this range, and there was a downward trend when the temperature rose. Therefore, the extraction temperature was tentatively selected at 50 °C for further optimization.

3.2. Optimization of Extraction Conditions Using RSM

Based on the single-factor tests mentioned above, three variables—ethanol concentration, extraction time, and extraction temperature—were selected as the guiding factors for further RSM optimization in the experiments, which affected the flavonoid yield and antioxidant activity in the extraction procedures.

A Box-Behnken design (BBD) of RSM was employed to investigate the effects of three variables—ethanol concentration (X_1), extraction temperature (X_2), and extraction time (X_3)—on the flavonoid yield (Y_1) and antioxidant activity (Y_2). The independent variables were coded at three levels (−1, 0 and 1), in detail, ethanol concentration (40%, 60%, and 80%), temperature (30, 50, and 70 °C) and extraction time (10, 20, and 30 min) were investigated (Table 1). This design was composed of 17 tested points, including five replications of the zero points (all variables were coded as zero), and the response results were obtained as shown in Table 2.

Table 1. Independent factors and their levels used in the response surface design.

Factors	Factor Level		
Coded levels	−1	0	1
A: Percentage of ethanol (%)	40	60	80
B: Extraction temperature (°C)	30	50	70
C: Extraction time (min)	10	20	30

Table 2. The experimental values for the responses of total flavonoids and 1,1-diphenyl-2-picrylhydrazyl (DPPH) scavenging at different levels.

Std.	Run	A (%)	B (°C)	C (min)	Total Flavonoids (mg/g)	DPPH Scavenging (%)
7	1	−1	0	1	208.95	55.45
9	2	0	−1	−1	217.19	58.07
1	3	−1	−1	0	229.66	53.85
10	4	0	1	−1	232.18	59.78
4	5	1	1	0	215.29	58.45
17	6	0	0	0	235.11	58.92
3	7	−1	1	0	232.24	58.09
6	8	1	0	−1	211.85	59.28
2	9	1	−1	0	218.87	58.17

Table 2. *Cont.*

Std.	Run	A (%)	B (°C)	C (min)	Total Flavonoids (mg/g)	DPPH Scavenging (%)
8	10	1	0	1	213.07	59.34
16	11	0	0	0	235.94	59.56
14	12	0	0	0	235.70	58.36
11	13	0	−1	1	234.40	57.31
15	14	0	0	0	229.99	58.50
12	15	0	1	1	228.62	58.74
13	16	0	0	0	240.65	59.89
5	17	−1	0	−1	221.54	55.02

3.3. Effect of Extraction Conditions on Flavonoid Yield and Antioxidant Activity

The average flavonoid yield and antioxidant activity of each of the 17 tests under the various experimental UAE conditions are shown in Table 2. The highest flavonoid yield of 240.65 mg/g and antioxidant activity of 59.89% were obtained in experimental run number 16, with 60% ethanol, a temperature of 50 °C, and a time of 20 min. The yield from this test was excellent compared to previous data. Two second-order regression equations were established to fit with this experiment as follow:

$$\text{Flavonoids yield} = 235.5 - 4.2A + 1.0B + 0.3C - 1.5AB + 3.5AC - 5.2BC - 12.9A^2 + 1.4B^2 - 8.8C^2, \quad (2)$$

$$\text{Antioxidant activity} = 59.0 + 1.6A + 0.96B - 0.2C - 1.0AB - 0.1AC - 0.1BC - 1.6A^2 - 0.4B^2 - 0.2C^2. \quad (3)$$

The expected regression coefficients and analysis of variance (ANOVA) of the flavonoid yield and antioxidant activity were presented using the BBD. A quadratic regression model of flavonoid yield was significant ($p < 0.05$), while the lack of fit was not significant ($p > 0.05$), suggesting that this model was highly consistent with the experimental results of the flavonoid yield. Similarly, the quadratic regression model of antioxidant activity was also feasible. The regression coefficients of the two indexes were $R^2 = 0.87$ and $R^2 = 0.91$, respectively, which indicated a good degree of consistency between the experimental data and the predicted yield. The calibration coefficients of the index model were $R^2_{Adj} = 0.70$ and $R^2_{Adj} = 0.80$, respectively, which indicated that the results were reliable.

3.4. Response Surface Analysis

Based on the equations mentioned above, three-dimensional (3D) surface values were depicted to show the influences of the UAE variables (ethanol concentration, extraction temperature, and extraction time) on the flavonoid yield and antioxidant activity (Figure 2).

The results for the combined effect of ethanol concentration and extraction temperature suggested that the effects of low and high levels of ethanol concentration and extraction temperature on the extraction were significant. When the extraction temperature was at a constant value, the flavonoid yield initially increased and then decreased with the increase in ethanol concentration. However, at a constant ethanol concentration, it was not significant that the increase in extraction temperature impacted the flavonoid yield (Figure 2A). From Figure 2B, the results indicated that the interactional effects between ethanol concentration and extraction time were remarkable when the other variables were set at a fixed value. From Figure 2C, it can be seen that when the extraction time was set at a constant value, the increase in extraction temperature had little influence on the flavonoid yield. However, when the temperature was constant, the flavonoid yield underwent a significant change, from a low level to a high level, with the increase in extraction time. The response surface suggested that the flavonoid yield showed a significant correlation with the ethanol concentration and extraction time, but little influence was obtained in relation to the extraction temperature. This was highly consistent with previous data from single-factor tests.

Similarly, for the antioxidant activity analysis, the results suggested that ethanol concentration and extraction temperature had a significant influence on the antioxidant activity of ZQ extract, with a low influence for extraction time (Figure 2D–F).

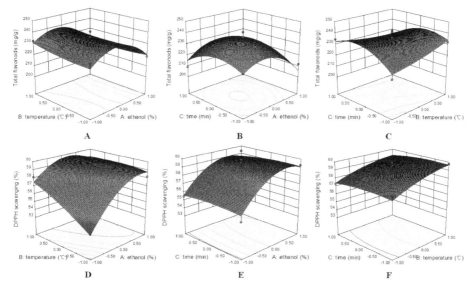

Figure 2. Response surface plots of ethanol concentration, extraction time, and temperature on the total flavonoids (**A–C**) and DPPH scavenging (**D–F**).

3.5. Theoretical Extraction Conditions and Verification

Based on the Design Expert software (Version10.0, Stat-Ease Inc., Minneapolis, MN, US), the desirability function of RSM was employed to obtain the optimal conditions for the flavonoid yield and antioxidant activity, and the optimum yield was achieved and set up with the following applied parameters: ethanol concentration, 58.4%; extraction temperature, 70 °C; and extraction time, 16.8 min. The estimated values were obtained (flavonoids, 239.04 mg/g; antioxidant activity, 59.59%).

The verification of the estimated results was validated using practical experiments under optimal conditions. The results indicated that the practical values (flavonoids, 241.70 mg/g; antioxidant activity, 59.42%) were consistent with the predicted values, the flavonoids yield was significant higher than previous reported data [15], and possessed high antioxidant activity at the same time. Therefore, the extraction conditions obtained using RSM were reliable and practical. The adjusted extraction conditions were: ethanol concentration, 58%; extraction temperature, 70 °C; and extraction time, 17 min. In contrast to traditional techniques, this model takes into account the interactions among several independent variables.

3.6. Identification of AFs from ZQ

The AFs from ZQ were identified using the HPLC–Q–TOF–MS method by comparing standards, fragmentation patterns and previously reported data [6] (Figure 3); flavanones and polymethoxyflavonoids (PMFs) were identified as the main AFs from ZQ (Table 3). In detail, flavanones including eriocitrin, neoeriocitrin, narirutin, naringin, hesperidin, neohesperidin, and poncirin, and PMFs including isosinensetin, sinensetin, nobiletin, 3,5,6,7,8,3′,4′-heptamethoxyflavone, and tangeretin were identified as the flavonoids with antioxidant properties. It was suggested that those antioxidant flavonoids might be effective ZQ ingredients for healthcare.

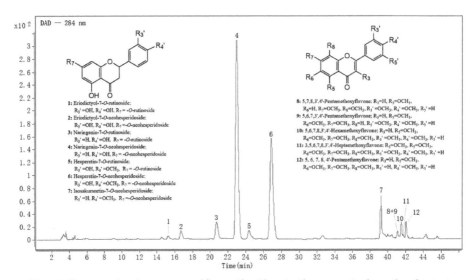

Figure 3. Representative chromatogram of flavonoids with antioxidant properties from ethanol extract of Aurantii fructus obtained using HPLC–DAD (λ = 284 nm) coupled with Q–TOF–MS.

Table 3. Mass spectrometry data of the main flavonoids with antioxidant properties from Aurantii fructus.

Number	Compound	[M+H]⁺/[M−H]⁻	Frag. (ESI+)	MW	Formula
Flavanones					
1	Eriodictyol-7-O-rutinoside (eriocitrin) [a]	597/595	435, 289	596	$C_{27}H_{32}O_{15}$
2	Eriodictyol-7-O-neohesperidoside (neoeriocitrin) [a]	597/595	435, 289	596	$C_{27}H_{32}O_{15}$
3	Naringenin-7-O-rutinoside (narirutin) [a]	581/579	419, 273	580	$C_{27}H_{32}O_{14}$
4	Naringenin-7-O-neohesperidoside (naringin) [a]	581/579	419, 273	580	$C_{27}H_{32}O_{14}$
5	Hesperetin-7-O-rutinoside (hesperidin) [a]	611/609	449, 303	610	$C_{28}H_{34}O_{15}$
6	Hesperetin-7-O-neohesperidoside (neohesperidin) [a]	611/609	449, 303	610	$C_{28}H_{34}O_{15}$
7	Isosakuranetin-7-O-neohesperidoside (poncirin) [a]	595/593	433, 287	594	$C_{28}H_{34}O_{14}$
Polymethoxyflavonoids (PMFs)					
8	5,7,8,3′,4′-Pentamethoxyflavone (isosinensetin)	373/—	358, 343, 315	372	$C_{20}H_{20}O_7$
9	5,6,7,3′,4′-Pentamethoxyflavone (sinensetin)	373/—	358, 343, 312	372	$C_{20}H_{20}O_7$
10	5,6,7,8,3′,4′-Hexamethoxyflavone (nobiletin) [a]	403/—	373, 355, 327	402	$C_{21}H_{22}O_8$
11	3,5,6,7,8,3′,4′-Heptamethoxyflavone	433/—	403, 388, 385	432	$C_{22}H_{24}O_9$
12	5, 6, 7, 8, 4′-Pentamethoxyflavone (tangeretin) [a]	373/—	358, 325, 297	372	$C_{20}H_{20}O_7$

[a] These compounds were accurately identified with reference standards.

3.7. Quality Evaluation of ZQ

The objective weight (W_j) according to the CRITIC method was expressed based on the characteristic conflict (R_j), the correlation of indicators (r_{ij}), the amount of information (C_j), and the standard deviation (σ_j). The calculated formulae were as follows:

$$R_j = \sum_{i=1}^{n}\left(1 - r_{ij}\right) \tag{4}$$

$$C_j = \sigma_j R_j \tag{5}$$

$$W_j = \frac{C_j}{\sum_{j=1}^{n} C_j} \tag{6}$$

The flavonoid yield and antioxidant activity of ZQs were determined, the data matrix was established according to the standardized data and formulae (experimental values − experimental minimum)/(experimental maximum − experimental minimum), and their objective weights were calculated according to the formulae mentioned above (Table 4).

Table 4. Comparison of intensity, conflict, information, and objective weight of evaluation indexes.

Evaluation Indexes	Intensity (σ_j)	Conflict (R_j)	Information (C_j)	Objective Weight (W_j)
Total flavonoids	0.231	0.358	0.083	0.440
DPPH scavenging	0.294	0.358	0.105	0.560

Then, according to the objective weight of the flavonoid yield and antioxidant activity, a qualitative evaluation method for ZQ was efficiently established, and the comprehensive scores of ZQ from different habitats were analyzed. As shown in Table 5, ZQ from *Sanyantang*, *Fuqiushan*, and *Chishanzhen* of Hunan Province showed excellent comprehensive scores and good quality levels.

Table 5. Comprehensive evaluation of Aurantii fructus from different areas in Hunan Province based on the intercriteria correlation (CRITIC) method ($n = 3$).

Samples	Region	Total Flavonoids (mg/g)	DPPH Scavenging (%)	Comprehensive Score	Ranking
S4	*Sanyantang, Yuangjiang*	356.53	75.34	97.33	1
S8	*Fuqiushan, Taojiang*	284.47	76.32	89.13	2
S6	*Chishanzhen, Yuangjiang*	264.36	79.11	88.63	3
S2	*Shijihu, Yuangjiang*	252.50	78.66	86.84	4
S9	*Heshanqu, Yiyang*	283.82	72.21	86.14	5
S11	*Nongda, Changsha*	277.24	71.82	85.05	6
S10	*Yangjixiang, Anren*	273.96	72.14	84.88	7
S7	*Longhushan, Yuangjiang*	249.72	74.54	83.58	8
S14	*Yanwanghuzhen, Hanshou*	242.64	75.77	83.58	9
S13	*Ningyuan, Yongzhou*	303.76	62.47	81.71	10
S15	*Bailuqiaozhen, Hanshou*	253.54	70.55	81.23	11
S5	*Tuanshanzhen, Yuangjiang*	231.88	74.06	81.04	12
S12	*Fenglinzhen, Lilin*	252.39	68.62	79.74	13
S16	*Xinning, Shaoyang*	212.36	61.70	69.88	14
S1	*Xinwanzhen, Yuangjiang*	182.99	55.25	61.69	15
S3	*Nanjuzhen, Yuangjiang*	151.23	51.24	54.94	16

4. Conclusions

This study clearly identified that the extraction processes of antioxidant flavonoids from ZQ could be improved by optimizing several key factors using RSM. Furthermore, the basic structures of potential antioxidant flavonoids were preliminarily illustrated using LC–Q–TOF–MS, and the comprehensive scores of AF quality from different habitats were then comparatively analyzed. As a raw material of TCM-HF, AFs of ZQ are an extract source with great potential for application in pharmaceutic preparations, functional food ingredients, dietary supplements, nutraceuticals, food additives, and so on.

Author Contributions: Y.H., H.X. and Q.T. conceived and designed the experiments; Y.H., Y.C., Y.S., H.T. performed the experiments and designed the figures; Y.H., Y.C., and Y.S. analyzed and helped in data interpretation; Q.T. collected the materials; Y.H. wrote the manuscript and K.Z. assisted language modification; J.Z. provided funding support; H.X. and Q.T. edited and supported suggestions for the manuscript.

Funding: This research was funded by the China Agriculture Research System (No. CARS-21), the Project of Hunan Science and Technology Innovation (No. S2017SFXYZ0116), the Major Projects of Hunan Provincial Science and Technology Department (No. 2015SK1001, 2014SK2005), the Project of Hunan Natural Science Foundation (No. 2017JJ2119), the Project of Hunan Postgraduate Research and Innovation (No. CX2016B311), the Science and Technology Project of Hunan Education Department (17A093), and National key laboratory cultivation base construction project (16KFXM15).

Conflicts of Interest: The authors declare no conflicts of interest.

References

1. Wai Chon Ng, H.H. From medicine to food: Evolution of TCM health food sector in China. *Int. J. Transit. Innov. Syst.* **2014**, *3*, 16.

2. Xu, Q.; Shen, Y.; Wang, H.; Zhang, N.; Xu, S.; Zhang, L. Application of response surface methodology to optimise extraction of flavonoids from fructus sophorae. *Food Chem.* **2013**, *138*, 2122–2129. [CrossRef] [PubMed]

3. Hou, W.; Zhang, W.; Chen, G.; Luo, Y. Optimization of Extraction Conditions for Maximal Phenolic, Flavonoid and Antioxidant Activity from Melaleuca bracteata Leaves Using the Response Surface Methodology. *PLoS ONE* **2016**, *11*, e0162139. [CrossRef] [PubMed]

4. *Pharmacopoeia of the People Republic of China*; Chinese Medical Science and Technology Press: Beijing, China, 2015.

5. Lin, Z.; Wang, H.; Xu, Y.; Dong, J.; Hashi, Y.; Chen, S. Identification of antioxidants in Fructus aurantii and its quality evaluation using a new on-line combination of analytical techniques. *Food Chem.* **2012**, *134*, 1181–1191. [CrossRef] [PubMed]

6. He, Y.; Li, Z.; Wang, W.; Sooranna, S.R.; Shi, Y.; Chen, Y.; Wu, C.; Zeng, J.; Tang, Q.; Xie, H. Chemical Profiles and Simultaneous Quantification of Aurantii fructus by Use of HPLC-Q-TOF-MS Combined with GC-MS and HPLC Methods. *Molecules* **2018**, *23*, 2189. [CrossRef] [PubMed]

7. He, Y.; Cheng, P.; Wang, W.; Yan, S.; Tang, Q.; Liu, D.; Xie, H. Rapid Investigation and Screening of Bioactive Components in Simo Decoction via LC-Q-TOF-MS and UF-HPLC-MD Methods. *Molecules* **2018**, *23*, 1792. [CrossRef] [PubMed]

8. Li, P.; Zeng, S.L.; Duan, L.; Ma, X.D.; Dou, L.L.; Wang, L.J.; Li, P.; Bi, Z.M.; Liu, E.H. Comparison of Aurantii Fructus Immaturus and Aurantii Fructus based on multiple chromatographic analysis and chemometrics methods. *J. Chromatogr. A* **2016**, *1469*, 96–107. [CrossRef] [PubMed]

9. Zhao, S.Y.; Liu, Z.L.; Shu, Y.S.; Wang, M.L.; He, D.; Song, Z.Q.; Zeng, H.L.; Ning, Z.C.; Lu, C.; Lu, A.P.; et al. Chemotaxonomic Classification Applied to the Identification of Two Closely-Related Citrus TCMs Using UPLC-Q-TOF-MS-Based Metabolomics. *Molecules* **2017**, *22*, 1721. [CrossRef]

10. He, Y.; Zhu, S.; Wu, C.; Lu, Y.; Tang, Q. Bioactivity-Guided Separation of Potential D_2 Dopamine Receptor Antagonists from Aurantii Fructus based on Molecular Docking Combined with High-Speed Counter-Current Chromatography. *Molecules* **2018**, *23*, 3135. [CrossRef]

11. Liu, X.Y.; Fan, M.L.; Wang, H.Y.; Yu, B.Y.; Liu, J.H. Metabolic profile and underlying improved bio-activity of Fructus aurantii immaturus by human intestinal bacteria. *Food Funct.* **2017**, *8*, 2193–2201. [CrossRef]

12. Su, M.S.; Shyu, Y.T.; Chien, P.J. Antioxidant activities of citrus herbal product extracts. *Food Chem.* **2008**, *111*, 892–896. [CrossRef]

13. Tan, W.; Li, Y.; Wang, Y.; Zhang, Z.; Wang, T.; Zhou, Q.; Wang, X. Anti-coagulative and gastrointestinal motility regulative activities of Fructus Aurantii Immaturus and its effective fractions. *Biomed. Pharmacother.* **2017**, *90*, 244–252. [CrossRef] [PubMed]

14. Kang, M.; Kim, J.H.; Cho, C.; Chung, H.S.; Kang, C.W.; Kim, Y.; Shin, M.; Hong, M.; Bae, H. Anti-ischemic effect of Aurantii Fructus on contractile dysfunction of ischemic and reperfused rat heart. *J. Ethnopharmacol.* **2007**, *111*, 584–591. [CrossRef] [PubMed]

15. Chen, J.Y.; Jia, W.; Zeng, Y.E.; Cao, C.; Wang, S.L. Optimal extracting conditions for flavonoids in Fructus Aurantii Immaturus with central composite design and response surface method. *Chin. J. Pharm. Anal.* **2012**, *32*, 5.

16. Mohamed Mahzir, K.A.; Abd Gani, S.S.; Hasanah Zaidan, U.; Halmi, M.I.E. Development of Phaleria macrocarpa (Scheff.) Boerl Fruits Using Response Surface Methodology Focused on Phenolics, Flavonoids and Antioxidant Properties. *Molecules* **2018**, *23*, 724. [CrossRef] [PubMed]

17. Zhou, D.Y.; Xing, R.; Xu, Q.; Xue, X.Y.; Zhang, F.F.; Liang, X.M. Polymethoxylated flavones metabolites in rat plasma after the consumption of Fructus aurantii extract: Analysis by liquid chromatography/electrospray ion trap mass spectrometry. *J. Pharm. Biomed. Anal.* **2008**, *46*, 543–549. [CrossRef] [PubMed]

18. Zhou, D.Y.; Xu, Q.; Xue, X.Y.; Zhang, F.F.; Jing, Y.; Liang, X.M. Rapid qualitative and quantitative analyses of flavanone aglycones in Fructus aurantii by HPLC ion-trap MS. *J. Sep. Sci.* **2007**, *30*, 858–867. [CrossRef]

19. Zhang, J.; Gao, W.; Liu, Z.; Zhang, Z.; Liu, C. Systematic Analysis of Main Constituents in Rat Biological Samples after Oral Administration of the Methanol Extract of Fructus Aurantii by HPLC-ESI-MS/MS. *Iran. J. Pharm. Res. IJPR* **2014**, *13*, 493–503.

20. Tomaz, I.; Maslov, L.; Stupic, D.; Preiner, D.; Asperger, D.; Karoglan Kontic, J. Multi-response optimisation of ultrasound-assisted extraction for recovery of flavonoids from red grape skins using response surface methodology. *Phytochem. Anal. PCA* **2016**, *27*, 13–22. [CrossRef]

21. Nipornram, S.; Tochampa, W.; Rattanatraiwong, P.; Singanusong, R. Optimization of low power ultrasound-assisted extraction of phenolic compounds from mandarin (*Citrus reticulata* Blanco cv. Sainampueng) peel. *Food Chem.* **2018**, *241*, 338–345. [CrossRef]

22. Liu, D.; Zhao, X. Method and application for dynamic comprehensive evaluation with subjective and objective information. *PLoS ONE* **2013**, *8*, e83323. [CrossRef] [PubMed]

23. Lay, M.M.; Karsani, S.A.; Banisalam, B.; Mohajer, S.; Abd Malek, S.N. Antioxidants, phytochemicals, and cytotoxicity studies on *Phaleria macrocarpa* (Scheff.) Boerl seeds. *BioMed Res. Int.* **2014**, *2014*, 410184. [CrossRef] [PubMed]

 *processes*

Article

Recycling of Carbon Fibers from CFRP Waste by Microwave Thermolysis

Jianying Deng [1], Lei Xu [1,2,*], Libo Zhang [1], Jinhui Peng [1], Shenghui Guo [1,2,*], Jianhua Liu [2] and Sivasankar Koppala [1]

[1] Faculty of Metallurgical and Energy Engineering, Kunming University of Science and Technology, Kunming 650093, China; jydengkust@163.com (J.D.); zhanglibopaper@126.com (L.Z.); jhpeng@kmust.edu.cn (J.P.); pepsiva9@gmail.com (S.K.)

[2] State Key Laboratory of Complex Nonferrous Metal Resources Clean Utilization, Kunming University of Science and Technology, Kunming 650093, China; liujianhua501050@163.com

* Correspondence: xulei_kmust@aliyun.com (L.X.); shguo78@hotmail.com (S.G.)

Received: 5 March 2019; Accepted: 8 April 2019; Published: 11 April 2019

Abstract: With the growth of the use of carbon fiber-reinforced polymer (CFRP) in various fields, the recovery of carbon fibers from CFRP waste is becoming a significant research direction. In the present work, degrading epoxy resin and recycling carbon fibers from CFRP waste by microwave thermolysis and traditional thermolysis were studied. The carbon fibers were successfully recovered by thermolysis under an oxygen atmosphere in this study. The properties of the recovered carbon fibers were characterized by field emission scanning electron microscopy (FESEM), Fourier transform infrared spectroscopy (FT-IR), X-ray diffraction (XRD), and Raman spectroscopy. The result shows that using microwave thermolysis to recover carbon fibers from CFRP waste is an attractive prospect. Compared to the traditional method, the reaction time was reduced by 56.67%, and the recovery ratio was increased by 15%. Microwave thermolysis is faster, more efficient, requires less energy, and obtains cleaner recovered carbon fibers than those recovered using traditional thermolysis.

Keywords: CFRP; recycling; carbon fibers; thermolysis; microwave

---

1. Introduction

Carbon fiber-reinforced polymer (CFRP) has been widely used in the aerospace, automobile, transportation, architecture, and sport industries, as well as the medical sector, due to their outstanding properties including low density, high strength and elastic modulus, and excellent resistance to corrosion and fatigue [1–5]. Carbon fibers were initially produced commercially starting in the late 1960s, and by 2006 approximately 27,000 tons of carbon fibers were being manufactured in industries around the world, an amount that will rise to 140,000 tonnes by 2020 [6,7]. CFRP is expected to be valued at over 25 billion dollars per year by 2025 [7]. However, the increasing use of CFRP has led to an increasing amount of waste being generated, consisting primarily of scraps and end-of-life components [1,8]. For instance, increasingly more plants using CFRPs will end their service life, generating massive amounts of CFRP waste [1,9–11]. Thus, the treatment of CFRP waste is becoming a more urgent problem.

Traditionally, CFRP waste has been managed by landfill disposal and incineration. However, it is predicted that traditional disposal approaches will need to be phased out due to pollution concerns, lack of economic viability, and new legal standards imposed in countries around the world [4,12,13]. Therefore, the recovery of carbon fibers from CFRP waste has become a research field that is attracting increasingly more attention. At present, various technologies have been proposed for recovering carbon fibers from carbon fibrefiber-reinforced epoxy resin composites with excellent characterization, including mechanical processes [14,15], chemical methods [4,16–20], and thermal technology [3,21–23].

However, long carbon fibers are difficult to obtain using a mechanical process, and their mechanical properties are seriously damaged with this technique [24,25]. Liu et al. [13], Yildirir et al. [19], and Hyde et al. [20] have investigated recycling carbon fibers from CFRP using different solvents under subcritical or supercritical conditions. These methods are expensive, difficult to industrialize, and produce large amounts of liquid waste and hazardous gases [1]. Yang et al. [3], López et al. [22], and Ye et al. [23] have studied thermolysis methods of recovering carbon fibers from CFRP. The pyrolysis process is not very economical, producing multiple hazardous gases and depositing char on the carbon fiber surfaces [1,19,25]. Therefore, research to develop new methods of recovering carbon fibers from CFRP has begun.

Microwave heating is gradually being used more often in the area of material processing due to its advantages of rapid, uniform, and selective heating [26]. Microwave heating is the process of coupling materials with microwaves, absorbing electromagnetic energy and transforming it into heat within the material volume, in which the heat is generated from the inside to the entire volume [27–29]. Therefore, the microwave method can treat uniform samples due to its features of volumetric and internal heating [30,31]. Yingguang Li et al. [32,33] have reported curing of CFRP by microwave energy, and CFRP can absorb microwave energy and be heated effectively. This study provides a great reference for microwave applications in the preparation and recovery of CFRP. Long Jiang et al. [34] reported that microwave irradiation is a flexible, easy-to-control, efficient method to recover high-value carbon fibers, and recovered carbon fibers could be directly used as reinforcement in new polymers (Polypropylene and nylon). This shows the great potential of effectively recycling carbon fiber by the microwave technique. In addition, Lester et al. [35] have reported carbon fiber recovery from polymer composites by microwave heating. Their results indicated that clean carbon fibers can be recovered using microwave heating, and that this method may be useful for recovering long carbon fibers [35]. However, these works have not undertaken enough research on the effects of different heating methods (microwave and traditional technique) on the recovery of carbon fibers. The research regarding the weight loss rate of CFRP, the recovery rate, and the chemical structure of recovered carbon fiber was not clear. In our present work, degradation of epoxy resin and recovery of carbon fibers from CFRP waste using microwave heating was studied. The influence of the reaction temperature and reaction time on carbon fiber recovery was investigated, and the surface of the carbon fibers was characterized.

2. Materials and Methods

2.1. Materials and Experimental Procedure

In this work, rectangular-shaped CFRP waste sheets with a thickness of 3 mm were provided by the Gongyi Fanruiyihui Composite Material Co., Ltd (Henan, China). The carbon fiber was Formosa Plastics TC33-3K, and the epoxy matrix was E51. The CFRP waste experiments were carried out in a high-temperature microwave furnace with a frequency of 2.45 GHz, under an oxygen atmosphere. In general, industrial microwave frequency is 2.45 GHz or 915 MHz [27,36]. However, most of the experiments regarding materials [27,28,37,38], metallurgical properties [27,30], or food [36,39] processing by microwaves are based on microwave magnetrons with 2.45 GHz frequency [28]. Therefore, the frequency of the microwave was selected as 2.45 GHz in this work. A K-type thermocouple was used to measure the temperature. The CFRP waste sheets were placed into a mullite crucible, which was placed within a polycrystalline mullite fiber cotton-based insulation chamber inside the microwave reactor. Oxygen was pumped continuously into the furnace cavity after the microwave furnace door was closed. Various microwave powers were applied to heat the CFRP waste, ultimately heating the samples from room temperature up to the desired reaction temperature, which was maintained for several minutes. In addition, the treatment of CFRP waste in a muffle furnace under an oxygen atmosphere was also examined. The microwave experimental process is shown in Figure 1.

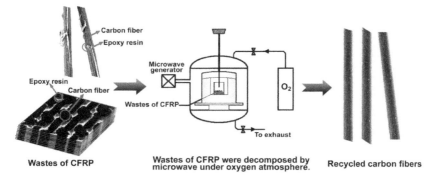

Figure 1. Schematic of carbon fiber-reinforced polymer (CFRP) waste treatment by microwave thermolysis.

2.2. Characterization

A Netzsch DSC/DTA-TG STA 449 F3 Jupiter®(Selb, Bavaria, Germany) was used to collect the thermogravimetric analysis (TGA) data. CFRP waste samples (10 mg) and virgin carbon fibers (10 mg) were heated individually from 30 °C to 1000 °C at 10 °C/min under an O_2 atmosphere (20 mL/min). The micro–morphologies and microstructures of the CFRP waste were examined using a metallographic microscope (Changfang CMM-10E, Shanghai, China) and scanning electron microscopy (SEM, Tescan VEGA3 SBH, Brno, Czech Republic). The surface images of recovered carbon fibers were examined using a field emission scanning electron microscope (FESEM, FEI Nova NanoSEM 450, Hillsboro, OR, USA). The functional groups of recovered carbon fibers were characterized by Fourier transform infrared spectroscopy (FT-IR, Thermo Scientific Nicolet iS50, Waltham, MA, USA), and the absorbance spectra were measured between 400 cm^{-1} and 4000 cm^{-1} using a Nicolet iS50 FT–IR spectrophotometer with a spectral resolution of 4 cm^{-1}. The crystalline phases of the recovered carbon fibers were observed by X-ray diffraction (XRD, PANalytical X' Pert3 Powder, Almelo, Overijssel, Holland). The XRD results were obtained using Cu Kα radiation with a scan rate of 8°/min in a 2θ of 5–70° at 40 kV and 40 mA. Raman spectra were obtained using a Renishaw plc. inVia Raman microscope (Gloucestershire, London, UK), with the laser power below 10.0 mW. The scanning wavenumber range was 800 cm^{-1} to 2300 cm^{-1}.

3. Results and Discussion

3.1. Characterization of Carbon Fiber-Reinforced Polymer (CFRP) by Metallographic Microscopy and Scanning Electron Microscopy (SEM)

The structure of the CFRP waste is shown in Figure 2. The CFRP waste sheets were rectangular in shape, measuring 18 × 18 × 3 mm. Figure 2a" shows the weave structure of carbon fibers, which indicates that the warp and weft were interwoven vertically. In the interwoven boundary of the carbon fiber bundles, it can clearly be seen that the carbon fibers are attached to each other by the epoxy resin.

The cross-sectional morphologies of CFRP waste are shown in Figure 2b–b". As shown in Figure 2b, approximately five layers of carbon fiber fabric were laminated, subsequently impregnated by epoxy resin (Figure 2b'), and then cured for a period of time [40]. The vertical and horizontal directionality of carbon fiber bundles alternated in the cross-section.

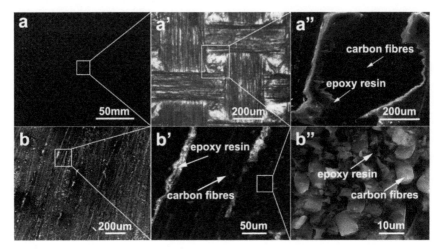

Figure 2. The structures of CFRP waste: (**a–a″**) surface structures, (**b–b″**) cross-sectional structures.

3.2. Thermal Decomposition Behavior of the CFRP Waste

The thermolytic behaviors of the CFRP waste and virgin carbon fibers under an oxygen atmosphere are shown in Figure 3. The thermolytic behavior of CFRP waste (Figure 3a) exhibited three oxidation peaks in the derivative thermogravimetric analysis (DTG) curve. The first peak corresponded to the degradation of the epoxy resin, the second peak corresponded to the oxidation of the pyrolytic carbon, and the third peak corresponded to the oxidation of the carbon fibers [3,41], indicating three reaction stages present in the TGA curve. The epoxy resin of the carbon fiber surface began to devolatilize at 230 °C with a mass loss of 11% at the end of first stage, the second devolatilization stage of the epoxy resin occurred between 350 °C and 550 °C with a mass loss of 38%, and the carbon fibers began to oxidize at 550 °C with 1.1% of residual mass. The differential scanning calorimetry (DSC) curve indicated that the reactions were exothermic. Figure 3b shows only one oxidation peak in the thermolysis behavior of virgin carbon fibers. Carbon fiber oxidation began at temperatures ranging from 500 °C to 600 °C and ended at 750 °C, with 1.3% of residual mass. This result was consistent with the result shown in Figure 3a. As shown in Figure 3c, the epoxy resin of the carbon fiber surface began to decompose at approximately 230 °C and stabilized at 450 °C, and this result was consistent with the results shown in Figure 3a,b. The temperature of the CFRP was 450 °C at 42 min. After 30 min duration, the residual mass of the CFRP was 66%, which was close to the 62% carbon fiber mass in the CFRP. Therefore, the durations were determined as 30 min in the muffle furnace. According to the TGA results, the reaction temperature (set between 400 °C and 500 °C in this study) was the critical factor for removing the epoxy resin of the carbon fiber surface and recovering carbon fibers. Some studies, such as Ye et al. [23] and Yang et al. [3], investigating the thermolytic process of recovering carbon fibers, have reported similar TGA results, so it was believed that the reaction temperature of the CFRP was relatively stable.

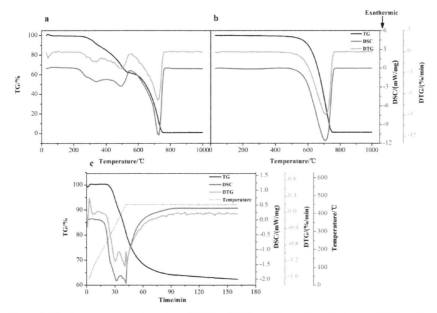

Figure 3. The thermogravimetric analysis (TGA) and differential scanning calorimetry (DSC) results under an oxygen atmosphere: (**a**) CFRP waste, (**b**) virgin carbon fibers, (**c**) CFRP waste maintained for 2 h at 450 °C.

The epoxy resin content in the CFRP waste was approximately 38 wt %. Table 1 shows the experimental details of the samples after treatment. The W_r, which was defined as the weight loss ratio of the CFRP waste, was calculated according to the following formula [3,19]:

$$W_r = \left(\frac{W_1 - W_2}{W_1}\right) \times 100\%$$ (1)

where W_1 and W_2 represent the weight of CFRP waste samples before and after experimentation, respectively.

Table 1. Details of samples under different reaction conditions.

Sample	Temperature/(°C)	Time/min	Average Power/W	Heating Method	Weight-Loss Ratio/%
1	400	30	850	Traditional	21.89
2	450	30	1060	Traditional	56.50
3	500	30	1300	Traditional	96.12
4	450	13	500	Microwave	47.03
5	450	30	500	Microwave	63.76

The R_{CF}, which was defined as the recovery ratio of carbon fibers, was calculated according to the following formula:

$$R_{CF} = \left(\frac{1 - W_r}{0.62}\right) \times 100\%$$ (2)

where W_r represents the weight loss ratio of the CFRP waste, and 0.62 is the mass of carbon fibers in the CFRP waste.

From Table 1, the best temperature should be between 400 °C and 450 °C, due to the 38 wt % weight-loss ratio being located between 400 °C and 450 °C. The weight-loss ratio of carbon fibers which were recovered by the microwave method at 450 °C was closer to 38 wt %, and required a shorter reaction time than that of carbon fibers which were recovered by the muffle furnace at the same temperature. Compared to the traditional method, the reaction time of the microwave method was reduced by 56.67% at 450 °C. The recovery ratios of the microwave and traditional method were approximately 85% and 70%, respectively. Thus, the microwave heating method is faster, has a better recovery ratio, and requires less energy than the traditional heating method.

3.3. Morphology of the Recovered Carbon Fibers

Figure 4 shows the recovered carbon fibers after traditional themolysis (Figure 4a–c) and microwave themolysis (Figure 4d). The epoxy resin could not completely decompose, with the sheet CFRP retained at 400 °C. However, it could be completely decomposed when the temperature reached 450 °C, and the carbon fibers could then be obtained. On the other hand, some of carbon fibers oxidized (the grey section in Figure 4c) when the temperature was above 500 °C. This result was consistent with the TGA results.

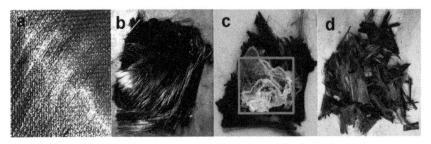

Figure 4. The macroscopic appearances of the CFRP waste samples after experiments: (**a**) 30 min of traditional heating at 400 °C, (**b**) 30 min of traditional heating at 450 °C, (**c**) 30 min of traditional heating at 500 °C, (**d**) 13 min of microwave heating at 450 °C.

The micromorphology of carbon fibers recovered by the traditional method is shown in Figure 5a–c. A small amount of epoxy resin is visible on the surface of the carbon fibers obtained at 400 °C. When the temperature was 450 °C, the carbon fibers' surfaces were relatively clean. However, when the temperature reached 500 °C, the surface of the carbon fibers were seriously damaged, exhibiting a large number of grooves indicative of partial oxidation on the carbon fiber surface. Thus, relatively clean carbon fibers could be recycled at 450 °C. From Figure 5d, we can see that the surface of the carbon fibers which underwent microwave heating at 450 °C were cleaner than those which were treated by traditional heating at the same temperature, and the reaction time was reduced by 56.67%. This conclusion was consistent with results of Table 1 and Figure 4.

Figure 5a'–d' shows the average diameter of the recovered carbon fibers. The average diameter of the virgin carbon fiber was around 7 μm. For the traditional method, the average diameter of the carbon fiber which was recovered at 400 °C for 30 min was 8.47 μm (Figure 5a') and at 450 °C for 30 min was 7.77 μm (Figure 5b'), which were both larger than the average diameter of virgin carbon fibers, possibly because the epoxy resin of the carbon fiber surface was not removed completely. However, when the temperature was 500 °C for 30 min, the average diameter of the recovered carbon fibers was 5.82 μm (Figure 5c') for the carbon fiber surface when oxidized. The average diameter of the carbon fiber which was recovered using the microwave method at 450 °C for 13 min was 7.02 μm (Figure 5d'), close to the virgin carbon fiber, which was probably due to the structure of the recovered carbon fiber not being damaged too much because of the microwave's rapid heating feature. However, the carbon fiber recovered by microwave at 450 °C for 30 min was damaged with many holes, as shown in Figure 5e,e'. Therefore, 13 min duration was chosen in the microwave furnace.

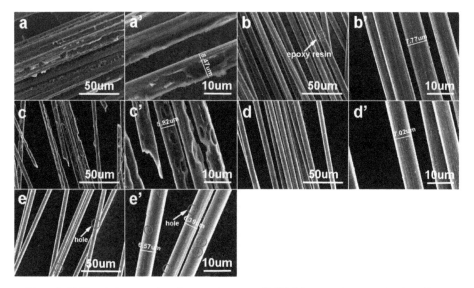

Figure 5. Field emission scanning electron microscope (FESEM) images of recovered carbon fibers: (**a**,**a′**) 30 min of traditional heating at 400 °C, (**b**,**b′**) 30 min of traditional heating at 450 °C, (**c**,**c′**) 30 min of traditional heating at 500 °C, (**d**,**d′**) 13 min of microwave heating at 450 °C, (**e**,**e′**) 30 min of microwave heating at 450 °C.

3.4. Fourier Transform Infrared (FT–IR) Analysis of the Recovered Carbon Fibers

Functional groups found on the recovered carbon fibers under different experimental conditions were observed in the FT-IR spectra, as shown in Figure 6, and alterations of major chemical bonds were also studied. Functional groups of carbon fibers usually include –CO, –OH, –COH and –COOH. The broad peak at 3420 cm^{-1} corresponded to O-H stretching vibrations due to water on the surface of the recovered carbon fibers. The small broad peak at 3260 cm^{-1} corresponded to O-H stretching vibrations related to hydroxyl groups. The peaks at 2960 cm^{-1} and 1380 cm^{-1} were attributed to the C-H stretching vibrations of a methyl group, while the peaks at 2930 cm^{-1} and 2850 cm^{-1} were attributed to the C-H stretching vibrations of a methylene group. The peaks at 2360 cm^{-1} and 2340 cm^{-1} were attributed to C≡N stretching vibrations. The peaks at 1630 cm^{-1} and 1084 cm^{-1} were attributed to the C=C and C-C stretching vibrations, respectively, of the recovered carbon fiber backbone. The peaks at 1260 cm^{-1} and 1050 cm^{-1} were C-O asymmetric and symmetric stretching vibrations, respectively.

From Figure 6, the FT-IR spectra of recovered carbon fibers were similar to those of virgin carbon fibers. However, the C≡N bands were produced on recycled carbon fibers, possibly due to curing during the preparation of CFRP. The C=C bands decreased, while the C-H bands and C-O bands increased, which was potentially because the reaction between the carbon atom and the oxygen atom broke down the C=C bonds and produced C-H bands and C-O bands. The FT-IR spectra of carbon fibers which were recovered using the traditional method from 400 °C to 500 °C for 30 min were similar, suggesting that an increase in the reaction temperature did not significantly impact the types of chemical bonds. However, the methyl peak became stronger and the C-O band increased while the C=C band decreased with a corresponding temperature increase, possibly due to the oxidation of carbon atoms and formation of C-O bonds. Compared with the traditional method, the types of chemical bonds of the recovered carbon fibers which were obtained using the microwave method did not noticeably change, but the intensity of its absorption peaks was weakened. This observation might be explained by the oxidation of more organic molecules to smaller molecules, which were released in the form of gas by microwave heating under an oxygen atmosphere. The FESEM results indicated that the recovered carbon fibers which were obtained at 450 °C by both the microwave and traditional methods were clean, while Figure 6 reveals that their C≡N bonds were small, possibly due to C≡N bond breakage related to epoxy resin of the carbon fiber surface removal.

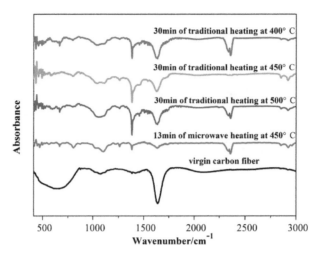

Figure 6. Fourier transform infrared (FT-IR) spectra of carbon fibers.

3.5. X-ray Diffraction (XRD) and Raman Analyses of the Recovered Carbon Fibers

The XRD results of the carbon fibers recovered under different conditions are shown in Figure 7a and 7b. A scattering peak is apparent in Figure 7a, indicating the (002) plane at approximately $2\theta = 25.5°$, reflecting the carbon layer stack thickness along the "c" axis (L_c). As illustrated in Figure 7b, another scattering peak was observed at the (101) plane at approximately $2\theta = 43.5°$, correlating to the graphite crystallite size along the "a" axis (L_a). The Raman spectra of the recovered carbon fibers are shown in Figure 8. The peak near 1370 cm^{-1} is called the D band, reflecting a graphitic lattice vibration mode with A_{1g} symmetry [4]. The other peak near 1600 cm^{-1} is the G band, reflecting an ideal graphitic lattice vibration mode with E_{2g} symmetry [4]. The β is the full width at the half-maximum of the peak with a unit of radian. W_D and W_G are the Raman shift of the D band and G band, respectively. A smaller integral intensity ratio R (I_D/I_G) indicates a higher degree of graphitization, or smaller proportions of the ordered structure of recovered carbon fibers [42].

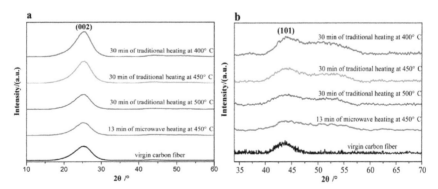

Figure 7. (**a**) XRD spectra of the (002) plane of carbon fibers, (**b**) XRD spectra of the (101) plane of carbon fibers.

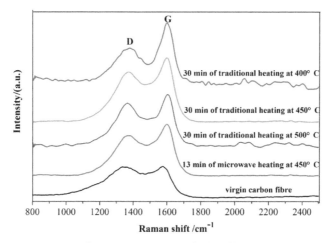

Figure 8. Raman spectra of carbon fibers.

Table 2 contains the crystallite parameters of the (002) plane and the (101) plane of the recovered carbon fibers in the XRD analysis. Upon comparison of carbon fibers which were recovered using the traditional method from 400 °C to 500 °C for 30 min, the value of β increased with increasing reaction temperature, which means the width of the scattering peaks increased, possibly due to the decrease in the crystallite size of the carbon fibers [43]. The intensity of the scattering peaks weakened significantly with increasing reaction temperature, indicating a reduction in the degree of graphitization. Comparison of the crystallite sizes (L_c and L_a) of the carbon fibers which were recovered using the traditional method from 400 °C to 500 °C showed that the size decreased obviously with an increase in temperature, revealing that the amount of amorphous carbon increased, demonstrating a lesser degree of graphitization and lower carbon fiber strength. This result was consistent with the conclusion obtained from Figure 7. Upon comparison of Samples 2 and 4, microwave heating had less influence on the degree of graphitization of recovered carbon fibers at 450 °C, due to the very similar values of L_c, and L_a. Compared with virgin carbon fibers, the properties of recycled carbon fibers decreased slightly. We believe that the reduction of graphitization is due to the increase of amorphous carbon, and the increase of amorphous carbon is due to temperature, and may also be the result of the intensified carbon combustion. In this study, we found this phenomenon, but the relationship between the decrease of graphitization degree, increase of amorphous carbon, temperature factor and carbon combustion still need to be further studied.

Table 2. X-ray diffraction (XRD) results of the (002) plane and the (101) plane of the recycled carbon fibers.

Sample	2θ (002)/°	D (002)/nm	2θ (101)/°	D (101)/nm	β (rad)	L_a/nm	L_c/nm
1	25.66	0.34684	43.52	0.20778	0.0898	3.06	1.57
2	25.60	0.34763	43.46	0.20804	0.0922	2.99	1.52
3	25.52	0.34879	43.42	0.20822	0.0963	2.73	1.46
4	25.54	0.34853	43.50	0.20789	0.0918	2.99	1.53
Virgin carbon fiber	25.36	0.35098	43.85	0.20631	0.0599	2.89	2.345

The Lorentz fitting parameters are listed in Table 3. Tuinstra et al. [44] studied the relationship between the value of R and L_a, concluding that $L_a = 4.4/R$. The L_a value of Raman was similar to the XRD results. At different temperatures with the traditional method from 400 °C to 500 °C, the D peak wave number values decreased and the R value increased with increasing reaction temperature, suggesting a reduced degree of graphitization of the recovered carbon fibers. This result indicated that increasing the reaction temperature caused greater damage to the structure of the recovered carbon fibers. Microwave thermolysis had little influence on the degree of graphitization of the recovered carbon fibers. The conclusions obtained from the Raman analysis were in very good agreement with the results of the XRD experiments.

Table 3. Raman results for the recycled carbon fibers.

Sample	$W_D/(cm^{-1})$	$W_G/(cm^{-1})$	$R\ (I_D/I_G)$	L_a/nm
1	1378.24	1598.61	1.19	3.70
2	1371.17	1598.61	1.55	2.84
3	1365.52	1602.85	1.64	2.68
4	1372.59	1598.61	1.59	2.76
Virgin carbon fiber	1363.6	1576.39	1.61	2.73

4. Conclusions

Using microwave and traditional thermolysis to degrade epoxy resin and recover carbon fibers from CFRP waste has been studied in this work. The result shows that carbon fibers can be recovered from CFRP waste using thermolysis at 450 °C under an oxygen atmosphere, and the best temperature for this is 450 °C in this study. Compared to traditional thermolysis, microwave thermolysis is a faster and more efficient method that requires less energy, achieving a reduced reaction time by 56.67% and an increased recovery ratio by 15%. Additionally, the surface of the carbon fibers recovered using microwave heating was cleaner, smoother, and contained less epoxy resin. Furthermore, the increase in amorphous carbon and a lessened degree of graphitization occurred with increasing temperature, corresponding to decreased carbon fiber strength. However, microwave heating has minimal influence on the graphitization degree when used at the same reaction temperature as that of the traditional heating method, and does not alter the chemical structure of the recovered carbon fibers.

It can be predicted that CFRP waste will be increasingly generated, and its disposal will become more and more urgent. At present, many methods have been researched to recycle CFRP waste. However, microwave energy has been shown to have unique advantages, and great application prospects for recycling CFRP due to being faster, more efficient, requiring less energy, and achieving a higher recovery ratio of carbon fibers than traditional heating. In the future, continuous microwave reactors and production lines should be investigated to recover CFRP industrially. In addition, although the reuse of carbon fibers has not been studied much, it should attract more and more attention. Recycled carbon fibers can maintain reasonable properties and meet the requirements of some fields, such as bearing, filling, and more. The reuse of carbon fibers requires low cost, expands the application field, and protects the environment, which are significant positive outcomes.

Author Contributions: Conceptualization, J.D., L.X., J.P. and S.G.; Data curation, J.D.; Formal analysis, J.D., L.X. and J.L.; Investigation, J.D.; Methodology, J.D., L.X., J.P. and S.G.; Project administration, L.Z.; Resources, L.X. and S.G.; Software, J.D. and J.L.; Supervision, L.X., L.Z., J.P. and S.G.; Validation, L.Z. and S.G.; Writing—original draft, J.D.; Writing—review and editing, L.X., S.G. and S.K.

Funding: This research was funded by National Natural Science Foundation of China: 51864030 & 51522405, National Key R&D Program of China: 2018YFC1901904, Yunnan Provincial Science and Technology Talents Program:2019HB003, Yunnan Science and Technology Major Project: 2018ZE008 and 2018ZE027, and Yunnan Provincial youth top-notch talent support program, Funding Scientific Research Fund of Kunming University of Science and Technology: KKZ3201752046.

Acknowledgments: Authors would like to acknowledge the National Natural Science Foundation of China, National Key R&D Program of China, Yunnan Provincial Science and Technology Talents Program, Yunnan Science and Technology Major ProjectYunnan Provincial youth top-notch talent support program, Scientific Research Fund of Kunming University of Science and Technology. Last but not least, the authors would like to thank the KUST in providing the research facilities to execute this research.

Conflicts of Interest: The authors declare no conflict of interest.

References

1. Sun, H.; Guo, G.; Memon, S.A.; Xu, W.; Zhang, Q.; Zhu, J.H.; Xing, F. Recycling of carbon fibers from carbon fiber reinforced polymer using electrochemical method. *Compos. Part A Appl. Sci. Manuf.* **2015**, *78*, 10–17. [CrossRef]

2. Oliveux, G.; Bailleul, J.L.; Gillet, A.; Mantaux, O.; Leeke, G.A. Recovery and reuse of discontinuous carbon fibres by solvolysis: Realignment and properties of remanufactured materials. *Compos. Sci. Technol.* **2017**, *139*, 99–108. [CrossRef]

3. Yang, J.; Liu, J.; Liu, W.; Wang, J.; Tang, T. Recycling of carbon fibre reinforced epoxy resin composites under various oxygen concentrations in nitrogen–oxygen atmosphere. *J. Anal. Appl. Pyrolysis* **2015**, *112*, 253–261. [CrossRef]

4. Xu, P.; Li, J.; Ding, J. Chemical recycling of carbon fibre/epoxy composites in a mixed solution of peroxide hydrogen and n,n-dimethylformamide. *Compos. Sci. Technol.* **2013**, *82*, 54–59. [CrossRef]

5. Frohs, W.; Jaeger, H. Carbon fiber & composite material—Landscape Germany. *Carbon* **2012**, *50*, 737.

6. Kraus, T.; Kühnel, M.; Witten, E. *Composites Market Report 2014 Market Developments, Trends, Challenges and Opportunities*; Federation of Reinforced Plastics: Frankfurt, Germany 2014.

7. Roberts, T. *The Carbon Fibre Industry: Global Strategic Market Evaluation 2006–2010*; Materials Technology Publications: Watford, Hertfordshire, UK, 2006; Volume 10.

8. Jiang, G.; Pickering, S.J.; Walker, G.S.; Wong, K.H.; Rudd, C.D. Surface characterisation of carbon fibre recycled using fluidised bed. *Appl. Surf. Sci.* **2008**, *254*, 2588–2593. [CrossRef]

9. Marsh, G. Reclaiming value from post-use carbon composite. *Reinf. Plast.* **2008**, *52*, 36–39. [CrossRef]

10. Mcconnell, V.P. Launching the carbon fibre recycling industry. *Reinf. Plast.* **2010**, *54*, 33–37. [CrossRef]

11. Roberts, T. Rapid growth forecast for carbon fibre market. *Reinf. Plast.* **2007**, *51*, 10–13. [CrossRef]

12. Jiang, G.; Pickering, S.J.; Lester, E.H.; Turner, T.A.; Wong, K.H.; Warrior, N.A. Characterisation of carbon fibres recycled from carbon fibre/epoxy resin composites using supercritical *n*-propanol. *Compos. Sci. Technol.* **2009**, *69*, 192–198. [CrossRef]

13. Liu, Y.; Shan, G.; Meng, L. Recycling of carbon fibre reinforced composites using water in subcritical conditions. *Mater. Sci. Eng. A* **2009**, *520*, 179–183.

14. Kouparitsas, C.E.; Kartalis, C.N.; Varelidis, P.C.; Tsenoglou, C.J.; Papaspyrides, C.D. Recycling of the fibrous fraction of reinforced thermoset composites. *Polym. Compos.* **2010**, *23*, 682–689. [CrossRef]

15. Ogi, K.; Shinoda, T.; Mizui, M. Strength in concrete reinforced with recycled cfrp pieces. *Compos. Part A Appl. Sci. Manuf.* **2005**, *36*, 893–902. [CrossRef]

16. Bai, Y.; Wang, Z.; Feng, L. Chemical recycling of carbon fibers reinforced epoxy resin composites in oxygen in supercritical water. *Mater. Des.* **2010**, *31*, 999–1002. [CrossRef]

17. Liu, Y.; Liu, J.; Jiang, Z.; Tang, T. Chemical recycling of carbon fibre reinforced epoxy resin composites in subcritical water: Synergistic effect of phenol and koh on the decomposition efficiency. *Polym. Degrad. Stab.* **2012**, *97*, 214–220. [CrossRef]

18. Yan, H.; Lu, C.X.; Jing, D.Q.; Chang, C.B.; Liu, N.X.; Hou, X.L. Recycling of carbon fibers in epoxy resin composites using supercritical 1-propanol. *Carbon* **2016**, *100*, 710–711. [CrossRef]

19. Yildirir, E.; Onwudili, J.A.; Williams, P.T. Recovery of carbon fibres and production of high quality fuel gas from the chemical recycling of carbon fibre reinforced plastic wastes. *J. Supercrit. Fluids* **2014**, *92*, 107–114. [CrossRef]

20. Hyde, J.R.; Lester, E.; Kingman, S.; Pickering, S.; Wong, K.H. Supercritical propanol, a possible route to composite carbon fibre recovery: A viability study. *Compos. Part A Appl. Sci. Manuf.* **2006**, *37*, 2171–2175. [CrossRef]

21. Yip, H.L.H.; Pickering, S.J.; Rudd, C.D. Characterisation of carbon fibres recycled from scrap composites using fluidised bed process. *Plast. Rubber Compos.* **2002**, *31*, 278–282. [CrossRef]

22. López, F.A.; Rodríguez, O.; Alguacil, F.J.; García-Díaz, I.; Centeno, T.A.; García-Fierro, J.L.; González, C. Recovery of carbon fibres by the thermolysis and gasification of waste prepreg. *J. Anal. Appl. Pyrolysis* **2013**, *104*, 675–683. [CrossRef]

23. Ye, S.Y.; Bounaceur, A.; Soudais, Y.; Barna, R. Parameter optimization of the steam thermolysis: A process to recover carbon fibers from polymer-matrix composites. *Waste Biomass Valorization* **2013**, *4*, 73–86. [CrossRef]

24. Piñero-Hernanz, R.; Dodds, C.; Hyde, J.; García-Serna, J.; Poliakoff, M.; Lester, E.; Cocero, M.J.; Kingman, S.; Pickering, S.; Wong, K.H. Chemical recycling of carbon fibre reinforced composites in nearcritical and supercritical water. *Compos. Part A Appl. Sci. Manuf.* **2008**, *39*, 454–461. [CrossRef]

25. Henry, L.; Schneller, A.; Doerfler, J.; Mueller, W.M.; Aymonier, C.; Horn, S. Semi-continuous flow recycling method for carbon fibre reinforced thermoset polymers by near- and supercritical solvolysis. *Polym. Degrad. Stab.* **2016**, *133*, 264–274. [CrossRef]

26. Peng, Z.; Lin, X.; Li, Z.; Hwang, J.Y.; Kim, B.G.; Zhang, Y.; Li, G.; Jiang, T. Dielectric characterization of indonesian low-rank coal for microwave processing. *Fuel Process. Technol.* **2017**, *156*, 171–177. [CrossRef]

27. Khaled, D.E.; Novas, N.; Gazquez, J.A.; Manzano-Agugliaro, F. Microwave dielectric heating: Applications on metals processing. *Renew. Sustain. Energy Rev.* **2018**, *82*, 2880–2892. [CrossRef]

28. Oghbaei, M.; Mirzaee, O. Microwave versus conventional sintering: A review of fundamentals, advantages and applications. *Cheminform* **2010**, *41*, 175–189. [CrossRef]

29. Yadoji, P.; Peelamedu, R.; Agrawal, D.; Roy, R. Microwave sintering of ni–zn ferrites: Comparison with conventional sintering. *Mater. Sci. Eng. B* **2003**, *98*, 269–278. [CrossRef]

30. Rybakov, K.I.; Buyanova, M.N. Microwave resonant sintering of powder metals. *Scr. Mater.* **2018**, *149*, 108–111. [CrossRef]

31. Kumar, R.C.; Benal, M.M.; Prasad, B.D.; Krupashankara, M.S.; Kulkarni, R.S.; Siddaligaswamy, N.H. Microwave assisted extraction of oil from pongamia pinnata seeds. *Mater. Today Proc.* **2018**, *5*, 2960–2964. [CrossRef]

32. Li, Y.; Li, N.; Zhou, J.; Cheng, Q. Microwave curing of multidirectional carbon fiber reinforced polymer composites. *Compos. Struct.* **2019**, *212*, 83–93. [CrossRef]

33. Li, Y.; Cheng, L.; Zhou, J. Curing multidirectional carbon fiber reinforced polymer composites with indirect microwave heating. *Int. J. Adv. Manuf. Technol.* **2018**, *97*, 1137–1147. [CrossRef]

34. Long, J.; Ulven, C.A.; Gutschmidt, D.; Anderson, M.; Balo, S.; Lee, M.; Vigness, J. Recycling carbon fiber composites using microwave irradiation: Reinforcement study of the recycled fiber in new composites. *J. Appl. Polym. Sci.* **2015**, *132*. [CrossRef]

35. Lester, E.; Kingman, S.; Wong, K.H.; Rudd, C.; Pickering, S.; Hilal, N. Microwave heating as a means for carbon fibre recovery from polymer composites: A technical feasibility study. *Mater. Res. Bull.* **2004**, *39*, 1549–1556. [CrossRef]

36. Guo, Q.; Sun, D.W.; Cheng, J.H.; Han, Z. Microwave processing techniques and their recent applications in the food industry. *Trends Food Sci. Technol.* **2017**, *67*, 236–247. [CrossRef]

37. Costa, C.; Santos, A.F.; Fortuny, M.; Araújo, P.H.H.; Sayer, C. Kinetic advantages of using microwaves in the emulsion polymerization of mma. *Mater. Sci. Eng. C* **2009**, *29*, 415–419. [CrossRef]

38. Fariñas, J.C.; Moreno, R.; Pérez, A.; García, M.A.; García-Hernández, M.; Salvador, M.D.; Borrell, A. Microwave-assisted solution synthesis, microwave sintering and magnetic properties of cobalt ferrite. *J. Eur. Ceram. Soc.* **2018**, *38*, 2360–2368. [CrossRef]

39. Chandrasekaran, S.; Ramanathan, S.; Basak, T. Microwave food processing—A review. *Food Res. Int.* **2013**, *52*, 243–261. [CrossRef]

40. Okajima, I.; Hiramatsu, M.; Shimamura, Y.; Awaya, T.; Sako, T. Chemical recycling of carbon fiber reinforced plastic using supercritical methanol. *J. Supercrit. Fluids* **2014**, *91*, 68–76. [CrossRef]

41. Jiang, G.; Pickering, S.J.; Walker, G.S.; Bowering, N.; Wong, K.H.; Rudd, C.D. Soft ionisation analysis of evolved gas for oxidative decomposition of an epoxy resin/carbon fibre composite. *Thermochim. Acta* **2007**, *454*, 109–115. [CrossRef]

42. Fei, J.; Duan, X.; Luo, L.; Zhang, C.; Qi, Y.; Li, H.; Feng, Y.; Huang, J. Grafting methyl acrylic onto carbon fiber via diels-alder reaction for excellent mechanical and tribological properties of phenolic composites. *Appl. Surf. Sci.* **2018**, *433*, 349–357. [CrossRef]

43. Khanna, R.; Ikram-Ul-Haq, M.; Cayumil, R.; Rajarao, R.; Sahajwalla, V. Novel carbon micro fibers and foams from waste printed circuit boards. *Fuel Process. Technol.* **2015**, *134*, 473–479. [CrossRef]

44. Tuinstra, F.; Koenig, J.L. Characterization of graphite fiber surfaces with raman spectroscopy. *J. Compos. Mater.* **1970**, *4*, 492–499. [CrossRef]

Article

Drying of Drill Cuttings: Emphasis on Energy Consumption and Thermal Analysis

Esra Tınmaz Köse

Department of Environmental Engineering, Çorlu Engineering Faculty, Namık Kemal University,
59860 Çorlu/Tekirdağ, Turkey; etinmaz@nku.edu.tr; Tel.: +90-282-250-23-57

Received: 26 December 2018; Accepted: 26 February 2019; Published: 7 March 2019

Abstract: Drill cuttings, contaminated with drilling fluids, are characterized by their high moisture content, which can cause problems for collection, storage, and transportation. Additionally, the practice of disposing waste with high moisture content into sanitary landfills is undesirable and mostly forbidden. For that reason, drying of waste with high moisture content, such as drill cuttings, is an essential operation. In this work, microwave and conveyor belt drying processes for drying drill cuttings containing water-based drilling fluids were examined in a lab-scale study. The results of the study indicated that the microwave dryer has been shown to be advantageous in terms of time and energy consumption for drying of thin film layers, while the conveyor drying system was more appropriate for bulk drying.

Keywords: drill cuttings; drying; energy; microwave; conveyor belt

---

1. Introduction

During drilling operations, it is necessary to keep the base clean by removing rock fragments and crumbs that are cut by the underground drill. During the drilling process, the structure formed by the rock fragments and crumbs cut by the drilling fluid is called interruption. Drill cuttings (DC) can have different characteristics depending on the purpose of the drilling, the characteristics and depth of the formations that are drilled through, and the characteristics of the drilling fluid used [1]. The waste produced from drilling operations consists of drill cuttings contaminated with drilling fluids [2].

The management of waste generated during oil-drilling in our country is carried out within the scope of Waste Management Regulation, which was published in the Official Gazette on 02.04.2015 and numbered as 29,314 [3]. According to regulation, drill wastes are defined by the section code "01 05—Wastes generated during the search, extraction, operation, and physical and chemical treatment of mines—drilling muds and other drilling wastes". Drilling wastes are considered as possibly dangerous waste, according to their properties and concentrations.

Drill cuttings are characterized by their high moisture content and low bulk density, which result in a low conversion efficiency as well as difficulties in its collection, storage, and transportation. The level of moisture content of drill cuttings is a critical factor that determines its disposal options [4–6].

The high moisture content of drill cuttings can cause them to have low calorific values. It is therefore not suitable for use in refused derived fuel (RDF) or direct combustion operations. Another waste-management practice is the use of drill cuttings as construction building materials. However, they are unable to be used as raw materials due to their high moisture content and irregular distribution of particle sizes. The final disposal method of drill cuttings, which are unlikely to be recovered, is sanitary landfilling. However, the regulations on the acceptance of liquid into landfill areas forms one of the most important problems in landfilling, as liquid wastes can only be taken if they are the result of specific analysis of wastewater treatment plants, or if they are re-injected into the well. The accumulation of all waste (solid–liquid) products in a single well causes the liquid waste to contain colloidal particles. Therefore, the injection method is not an acceptable option since injection of these particles can affect production values. The temporary storage of liquid wastes in large pools is another method of waste-management. However, the long-term management of accumulated liquid waste can lead to larger problems. Therefore, taking into account the obligation of Article 9 (a) of the Waste Management Regulation [3], and Article 8 (a) of the Mining Waste Regulation [7], measures should be taken to minimize the amount of waste produced instead [8].

The drying process is an effective solution, which reduces the weight and volume of the sludge and reduces transportation and management costs, thus allowing for the easy handling, preservation, and storage of the wastes [6,9].

Drying refers to the process of thermally removing volatile substances (moisture) to yield a solid product. During the drying of wet solids, two separate processes occur simultaneously:

- Process 1—the transfer of energy (mostly as heat) from the surrounding environment to evaporate surface moisture;
- Process 2—the transfer of internal moisture to the surface of the solid and its subsequent evaporation due to Process 1 [9].

In Process 1, the removal of water from solid material as vapor occurs from the surface of the material depending on the external conditions of temperature, pressure, area of exposed surface, air humidity, and flow. In Process 2, the movement of moisture internally within the solid material depends on the physical nature, temperature, and initial moisture content of the material. While these two processes occur simultaneously during the drying process, one of the processes may be a limiting factor [9]. Drying is a complicated process that involves simultaneous heat and mass transfer, accompanied by physicochemical transformations. Based on the mechanism of heat transfer that is employed, drying is categorized into direct (convection), indirect or contact (conduction), radiant (radiation), and dielectric or microwave (radio frequency) drying. Although more than 85% of industrial dryers are of the convective type, contact dryers offer higher thermal efficiency and have economic and environmental advantages over convective dryers [10,11]. Rising energy costs, compulsory legislation on pollution, working conditions, and safety, have a direct bear upon the design as well as selection of dryers [9]. Table 1 shows the classification of dryers based on various criteria [9–12].

Table 1. Classification of dryers.

Criterion	Types
Mode of operation	Batch, continuous
Heat input type	Convection, conduction, radiation, electromagnetic fields, combination of heat transfer modes intermittent or continuous adiabatic or non-adiabatic
State of material in dryer	Stationary moving agitated, dispersed
Operating pressure	Vacuum, atmospheric
Drying medium (convection)	Air, superheated steam flue gases
Drying temperature	Below boiling temperature, above boiling temperature, below freezing point
Relative motion between drying medium and solids	Co-current countercurrent mixed flow
Number of stages	Single multistage
Residence time	Short (60 min)

In this work, an experimental study was performed on the drying of drill cuttings containing water-based drilling fluids with the two drying systems—microwave and conveyor belt dryers. There have been many studies previously conducted on the process of microwave drying drill cuttings.

In microwave drying systems, mass and treatment time directly relate to specific energy [2]. In previous literature, it was emphasized that microwave drying was a cost-effective and time-efficient system for the management of waste that was contaminated with petroleum hydrocarbons [2,6,13–20]. It also has several advantages with respect to the environment such as being a cleaner energy source, and being more energy-saving [6,21–24]. Conveyor belt dryers are versatile and suitable dryers for drying of varied products such as nuts, animal feeds, briquettes, rubbers [25], and biofuels [26]. Hot air is forced up through the product while it is carried through the dryer on conveyors [9,25]. Conveyor belt dryers are preferable drying systems for industrial applications, however, studies in the literature regarding drying of drill cuttings with conveyor belt dryers are quite limited. The aim of this study was to compare these two drying systems in respect of drying time and energy consumption. There are no studies on the drying of drill cuttings resulting from drilling operations occurring in the Thrace Region, and the material used in this study is original because of two different reasons. The first reason is that the properties of drill cuttings differ depending on the geological formation of the drilling area. The region where the drill cuttings are provided is located on five different bases starting from the Eocene in the Thrace Basin. These bases are Istranca massif and Upper Cretaceous Volcanics (Yemislicay Formation) in the North, Paleozoic sediments in the East, and the Sakarya and Intra-Pontide Suture Zones in the South. The location where the sample was collected mostly from was Istranca metamorphics [27]. Changes in geological formation at different locations, even in the same area, cause changes in the properties of drill cuttings. Properties of drilling fluid are the second reason why drill cuttings used in this study were original materials. During the preparation of the water-based drilling fluid, a large amount of water was absorbed by the clay and a suspension was formed in the drilling fluid formed by the mixture of water, clay (bentonite), and other chemicals. Some free-water circulated in this suspension. While the free-water is easily removed from drill cutting by heat, it is more difficult to remove the water absorbed by the clay [28]. This shows the difference between the materials used in this study, and the materials that are subject to many other studies in the literature.

2. Materials and Methods

2.1. Material Characterization

A sample of drill cuttings containing water-based drilling fluids was obtained from hydrocarbon drilling operations conducted in the Thrace Region of Turkey. The characterization study of drill cuttings was accomplished in the prior project of the author of [27]. Table 2 shows the parameters analyzed and the analysis methods used on them. X-ray fluorescence (XRF) data for major oxides and elements, BTEX, PCBs, mineral oil contents, total organic carbon, dissolved organic carbon, total dissolved solid and conductivity values are given in Tables 3 and 4.

Table 2. Parameters analyzed and analysis methods.

Parameter	Analytical Method
DOC (Dissolved organic carbon)	SM-5310 B High-temperature combustion method
TDS (Total dissolved solid)	SM-2540 C gravimetric method
TOC (Total organic carbon)	SM-5310 B High-temperature combustion method
Conductivity	ASTM D1125-14
BTEX	EPA-8015C Nonhalogenated organics using GC/FID
PCBs	ISO 10382 GC method with electron capture detection
Mineral oil (C10–C40)	BS EN 14039
Chemical properties moisture content	X-Ray fluorescent spectrometer (XRF) ASTM 3173

Table 3. Chemical composition of drill cuttings.

Element	%	Oxide	%	Element	%	Oxide	%
O	41.590			Ti	0.362	TiO_2	0.605
Na Mg	2.150	Na_2O_3	2.898	Cr	0.041	Cr_2O_3	0.060
Mg	2.482	MgO	4.115	Mn	0.084	MnO	0.108
Al	7.150	Al_2O_{33}	13.509	Fe	3.952	Fe_2O_3	5.650
Si	21.482	SiO_2	45.958	Co	0.012	Co_3O_4	0.016
P	0.070	P_2O_5	0.161	Ni	0.017	NiO	0.022
S	0.506	SO_3	1.263	Cu	0.042	CuO	0.053
Cl	3.009	Cl	3.009	Zn	0.011	ZnO	0.014
K	4.565	K_2O	5.499	Ba	1.394	BaO	1.557
Ca	11.080	CaO	15.503				

Table 4. Chemical properties of drilling cutting.

Parameter	Unit	Value
BTEX	mg/kg	<0.5
PCBs	mg/kg	<0.1
Mineral oil (C10–40)	mg/kg	1247
TOC	%	0.7228
DOC	mg/L	209.79
TDS	mg/L	2.810
Conductivity	S/cm	4380
Moisture content	%	45 ± 2

According to the results of the measurements, the element with the highest percentage by weight of total mass was silicon (Si) with 21.482%, followed by calcium (Ca) with 11.080%. Oxide ratios of the same elements were determined as 45.958% for SiO_2, and 15.503% for CaO. Al and Al_2O_3 ratios of drill cuttings were 7.150% and 13.509% respectively. The BTEX, PCB and mineral oil concentrations were measured as 0.5 mg/kg, lower than 0.1 mg/kg and 1247 mg/kg, respectively. Initial moisture content of drill cuttings was measured as 45 ± 2%.

2.2. Experimental Setup

A programmable microwave oven (Arçelik MD 554, Turkey) with maximum output of 800 W at a frequency of 2450 MHz was used for microwave drying experiments. The scheme of the microwave oven is illustrated in Figure 1. The dimensions of the microwave inner case were $455 \times 281 \times 325$ mm. Three different microwave output powers (120, 350, and 600 W) were taken into consideration in the drying experiments.

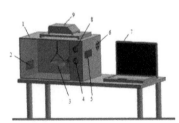

Figure 1. Microwave drying system: (**1**) Microwave oven, (**2**) ventilation holes, (**3**) tray, (**4**) timer, (**5**) magnetron, (**6**) fan, (**7**) computer, (**8**) power switch, (**9**) scales.

The other drying system used in the study was the conveyor dryer with dimensions of 2370 $\times$ 50 $\times$ 40 mm and with 2000 W heating power. Drying experiments were performed at 3 different temperatures (70 °C, 80 °C, and 90 °C) and a constant band speed of 0.12 m/min. The scheme of the conveyor dryer is given in Figure 2.

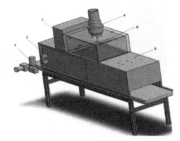

Figure 2. Conveyor drying system: (**1**) Electric motor, (**2**) drying room, (**3**) control panel, (**4**) fan, (**5**) heater, (**6**) ventilation hole.

Samples were taken, periodically, from each drying system in order to measure their average weight with a Presica XB 620 M (Precisa Instruments AG, Dietikon, Switzerland). The energy consumption of the microwave oven was determined using a digital electric counter with 0.01 kW h precision. Temperature change photographs of drill cuttings were taken with the thermal imager (Flir Ex E6, Estonia) before starting the experiments, and during the drying processes. Moisture content of the samples were measured within an INGDA KH-35A (China) brand oven.

2.3. Experimental Procedure

At the beginning of the drying experiments, the drill cuttings were homogenized by mixing. All drying tests were carried out in 50 g, 100 g, and 150 g samples. Microwave drying experiments were carried out at 120 W (at 2 min intervals), at 350 W (at 1 min intervals), and at 600 W (at 2 min intervals) microwave power levels.

Conveyor drying experiments were carried out at 70 °C (at 60 min interval), 80 °C (at 30 min interval), and 90 °C (15 min interval) at a constant belt speed of 0.12 m/min and at constant air velocity of 1 m/s.

Sample weights were measured at all powers, drying temperatures in both drying systems, and thermal images of the samples were taken. The thermal images showed the regions where the samples were most heated and whether they were homogeneous or not.

The moisture content on the wet base was defined as the ratio of water weight in the sample to the total weight of the sample. Equation (1) was used to calculate the moisture content on wet base [29,30].

$$m = \frac{M_w}{M_w + M_s} \tag{1}$$

where M_w (g) was the weight of water in the sample and M_s (g) was the weight of the dry sample.

Energy consumption was measured and recorded to determine the energy consumption of each dryer by means of the energy measurement device at the measurement periods. The studies were done with three replicates at all power, and drying temperatures.

3. Results and Discussion

3.1. Drying Characteristics

Drying experiments were completed when the drill cuttings were completely dried. Drying processes were applied until the weight of the sample reduced to a level corresponding to moisture content of approximately 13.5 ± 0.5% on a wet basis for microwave drying, and approximately 13.5 ± 0.3% on wet basis for conveyor belt drying, while the initial moisture content of drill cuttings were approximately 42 ± 2%. The variation in the moisture content of drill cuttings for different weights in respect to the wet base are given in Figure 3 for the microwave dryer, and Figure 4 for the conveyor belt dryer.

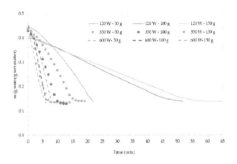

Figure 3. Variation of moisture content of drilling cutting for microwave dryer.

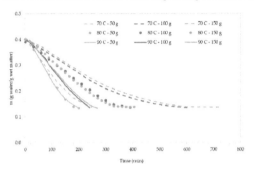

Figure 4. Variation of moisture content of drilling cutting for conveyor belt dryer.

According to results, it was clear that the drying time in the microwave dryer was influenced by microwave power. Moisture loss accelerated and drying time was shortened with increased microwave power. The drying times of the microwave dryer for 120, 350, and 600 W microwave powers were; 22, 14, and 8 min, respectively, for 50 g samples; 52, 13, and 12 min for 100 g samples, and 65, 19, and 8 min for 150 g samples. Past studies have showed that drying times for microwave drying of hydrocarbon drilling sludge decreased with increasing microwave power levels, whereas drying time increased with increasing layer thickness of the sample [6,31]. Tınmaz Köse et al. [6] reported that drying times were found as 8.5, 2.5, and 2 s for 50 g samples; 37.5, 6.5, and 5 s for 150 g samples at 120, 460, and 600 W, respectively. Tınmaz Köse et al. [31] concluded that when microwave power level was increased from 120 W to 700 W, the drying time decreased from 48 min to 5.5 min. The results obtained in this study were consistent with data from previous literature.

For conveyor belt dryers, it was determined that drying temperature was effective on the moisture content of drill cuttings and drying times were decreased with increasing drying temperature. The drying times of conveyor dryers at 70 °C, 80 °C, and 90 °C temperatures were 270, 200, and 195 min for 50 g samples, respectively; 240, 390, and 600 min for 100 samples, and 270, 405, and 720 min for 150 g samples.

The working mechanisms of the two dryers were different. In microwave applications, microwaves can transport energy to the entirety of the material, as energy affects the internal structure. This is the main reason why microwave drying systems shorten drying times.

3.2. Energy Consumption

Energy consumptions of the microwave dryer at different microwave power levels are given in Figure 5, and energy consumptions of the conveyor dryer at different drying temperatures are shown in Figure 6. During the drying period, energy consumptions were measured and recorded with an energy meter for both drying systems. Energy consumptions of the microwave dryer for 120, 350, and 600 W microwave powers were 0.33, 0.13, and 0.13 kWh for 50 g samples, respectively; 0.78, 0.13, and 0.18 kWh for 100 g samples, and 0.65, 0.19, and 0.12 kWh for 150 g samples. Energy consumptions of the conveyor dryer to reach the drying temperatures of 70 °C, 80 °C and 90 °C were 0.45 kWh, 0.95 kWh, and 1.21 kWh, respectively. At the end of the drying process, energy consumptions of the conveyor dryer at 70 °C, 80 °C and 90 °C temperatures were 6.80, 4.08, and 7.02 kWh minutes for 50 g samples, respectively; 14.65, 6.76, and 8.35 kWh for 100 samples, and 16.75, 13.59, and 10.41 kWh for 150 g samples.

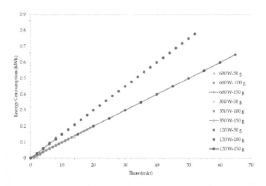

Figure 5. Energy consumption of the microwave dryer at different microwave power levels.

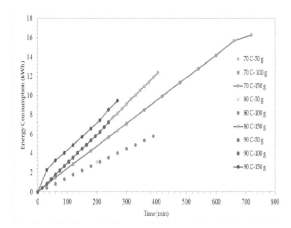

Figure 6. Energy consumption of the conveyor dryer at different drying temperatures.

Previous studies [6,31] reported that energy consumption values for microwave drying of hydrocarbon drilling sludge decreased with increasing microwave power levels because of decreasing drying time. Tınmaz Köse et al. [6] found that energy consumptions values for microwave power levels of 120 W, 460 W, and 600 W were recorded as between 0.03 and 0.11 kWh, 0.02 and 0.08 kWh, and 0.01 and 0.07 kWh, respectively. Tınmaz Köse et al. [31] determined that energy consumptions for microwave power levels of 700 and 120 W were 0.11 and 0.16 kW/h, respectively. The results obtained in the study were consistent with previous literature.

Conveyor drying systems are open systems while microwave drying systems are closed systems. Heat losses in closed systems are less than heat losses in open systems. While open systems such as conveyor systems have insulated systems to prevent heat loss, openings of input and output structures causes heat loss. The heaters must operate continuously to prevent the loss of ambient temperature with heat loss. This situation causes the energy consumption of the conveyor drying systems to be high.

3.3. Thermal Analysis

Images and thermal images of drill cuttings at the beginning of the study (wet state at room temperature), during the drying process, and at the end of the study (dry state) were taken and recorded. A scale showing the minimum and maximum temperature values of photographs and thermal images are given in S1–S6. At the end of the experiments, the temperatures of dried samples were measured between 22.1 °C and 194 °C for the microwave dryer, and between 22.3 °C and 84.8 °C for the conveyor dryer.

High energy absorption and high drying rates led to local overheating during the drying process. Overheating caused excessive localization and made control difficult [31]. Increasing microwave power levels resulted with an increased temperature of the final product. In some areas the color appeared as yellow. These areas were where the product continued to warm up. Microwave energy acted on water molecules in the product and caused heat to be released by vibrating water molecules [32]. As a result of this, increased temperature was observed in the product, especially in the center. The red color on the sides indicated that the liquid part of the slurry flowed sideways, and that there was an excess of energy caused by this [32].

According to thermal images taken during the study, the drying process occurred homogenously. Generally, the same temperature values were observed on the surface of the drill cuttings, as the temperatures in the conveyor drying process acted on the surface. The observed temperature differences were related to the fact that the homogeneous structure of drill cuttings was not fully achieved.

4. Conclusions

Drying of drill cuttings is an effective waste management step for the reduction in transportation and management costs, supplying needs of easy handling, preservation, and storage of such waste. However, drying time and energy consumption are limiting factors in decisions surrounding suitable drying technology.

While microwave drying systems have great advantages in terms of energy consumption for thin layer drying processes, they are not suitable for drying bulk materials. When drying bulk materials, it is difficult to penetrate microwave energy into bulk materials and, therefore, drying will not occur in the internal side of the materials. In this study, the drying of samples of 50, 100, and 150 g weights, with a layer thickness of 1 cm, was determined according to the penetration depth of microwave energy, as was performed. As a result of the operating mechanism of the microwave drying processes, the drying process was carried out quickly due to the homogeneous distribution of energy in thin layer drying, and thus, the moisture was quickly removed from the material. The temperature changes of material during the drying period were proven by thermal images.

During drilling operations, a considerable amount of drill cuttings occurred. Thin layer drying may not be an applicable and economic practice for excess amounts of drill cuttings. For that reason, when considering which drying method to apply, the amount of drill cuttings should be considered.

In this study, according to results of the experiments carried out to determine the most suitable drying process, it was concluded that it would be more appropriate to prefer conveyor dryers in case of bulk drying, while providing the appropriate results for thin film layer drying by microwave dryers.

Funding: This research received no external funding.

Conflicts of Interest: The author declares no conflict of interest.

References

1. Geology Information Page, Environmental Geology, Drilling Fluid (Drilling Sludge). Available online: http://www.jeolojitr.com/2014/09/sondaj-sivilari-sondaj-camuru.html#more (accessed on 12 December 2018).
2. Pereira, M.S.; Panisset, C.M.A.; Martins, A.L.; Sá, C.H.M.; Barrozo, M.A.S.; Ataíde, C.H. Microwave treatment of drilled cuttings contaminated by synthetic drilling fluid. *Sep. Purif. Technol.* **2014**, *124*, 68–73. [CrossRef]
3. Anonym, Waste Management Regulation, Official Gazette, Official Gazette Time: 02.04.2015 Official Gazette Number:29314. Available online: http://www.mevzuat.gov.tr/Metin.Aspx?MevzuatKod=7.5.20644&MevzuatIliski=0&sourceXmlSearch=at%C4%B1k%20y%C3%B6netimi (accessed on 15 December 2018). (In Turkish)
4. Tao, T.; Peng, X.F.; Lee, D.J. Skin layer on thermally dried sludge cake. *Drying Tech.* **2006**, *24*, 1047–1052. [CrossRef]
5. Zhang, X.Y.; Chen, M.Q.; Huang, W.; Xue, F. Isothermal hot air drying behavior of municipal sewage sludge briquettes coupled with lignite additive. *Fuel* **2016**, *171*, 108–115. [CrossRef]
6. Tınmaz Köse, E.; Çelen, S.; Çelik, S.Ö. Conventional and microwave drying of hydrocarbon cutting sludge. *Environ. Prog. Sustain. Energy* **2018**. [CrossRef]
7. Anonym, Mining Waste Regulation, Official Gazette, Official Gazette Time: 15.07.2015 Official Gazette Number: 29417. Available online: http://www.mevzuat.gov.tr/Metin.Aspx?MevzuatKod=7.5.20913&MevzuatIliski=0&sourceXmlSearch=maden%20at%C4%B1k (accessed on 15 December 2018). (In Turkish)
8. Doğanay, G. 2018, Sondaj Atıkları ve Yönetmeliklere Göre Atık Yönetimi. Available online: http://medyaenerji.com/2018/02/14/sondaj-sektorunde-cevre-mevzuati/ (accessed on 15 December 2018). (In Turkish)
9. Mujumdar, A.S. *Handbook of Industrial Drying Industrial, Drying Handbook of Fourth Edition*; CRC Press, Taylor & Francis Group: Boca Raton, FL, USA; London, UK; New York, NY, USA, 2015.
10. Parikh, D.M. Solids Drying: Basics and Applications, Website of Chemical Engineering. Available online: https://www.chemengonline.com/solids-drying-basics-and-applications/?printmode=1 (accessed on 14 December 2018).
11. Rossi, A.S.; Faria, M.G.; Pereira, M.S.; Ataide, C.H. Kinetics of microwave heating and drying of drilling fluids and drill cuttings. *Dry Technol.* **2017**, *35*, 1130–1140. [CrossRef]
12. Mujumdar, A.S. Drying: Principles and Practice. In Proceedings of the International Workshop on Drying of Food and Biomaterials, Bangkok, Thailand, 6–7 June 2011.
13. Sahnia, E.K.; Chaudhuria, B. Contact drying: A review of experimental and mechanistic modeling approaches. *Int. J. Pharm.* **2012**, *434*, 334–348. [CrossRef] [PubMed]
14. Júnior, I.J.; Pereira, M.S.; Santos, J.M.; Duarte, C.R.; Ataíde, C.H.; Panisset, C.M.S. Microwave remediation of oil well drill cuttings. *J. Petrol. Sci. Eng.* **2015**, *134*, 23–29.
15. Júnior, I.P.; Leibsohn Martins, A.; Ataíde, C.H.; Duarte, C.R. Microwave drying remediation of petroleum-contaminated drill cuttings. *J. Environ. Manag.* **2017**, *196*, 659–665. [CrossRef] [PubMed]
16. Shang, H.; Snape, C.E.; Kingman, S.W.; Robinson, J.P. Microwave treatment of oil-contaminated north sea drill cuttings in a high power multimode cavity. *Sep. Purif. Technol.* **2006**, *49*, 84–90. [CrossRef]
17. Rossi, A.S.; Pereira, M.S.; dos Santos, J.M.; Petri, I.; Ataíde, C.H. Fundemantals of microwave heating and drying of drilled cuttings. *Mater. Sci. Forum* **2017**, *899*, 528–533. [CrossRef]
18. Chien, Y. Field study of in situ remediation of petroleum hydrocarbon contaminated soil on site using microwave energy. *J. Hazard. Mater.* **2012**, *199–200*, 457–461. [CrossRef] [PubMed]
19. Robinson, J.P.; Kingman, S.W.; Onobrakpeya, O. Microwave-assisted stripping of oil contaminated drill cuttings. *J. Environ. Manag.* **2008**, *88*, 211–218. [CrossRef] [PubMed]
20. Robinson, J.P.; Kingman, S.W.; Snape, C.E.; Barranco, R.; Shang, H.; Bradley, M.S.A.; Bradshaw, S.M. Remediation of oil-contaminated drill cuttings using continuous microwave heating. *Chem. Eng. J.* **2009**, *152*, 458–463. [CrossRef]
21. Proestos, C.; Komaitis, M. Application of microwave-assisted extraction to the fast extraction of plant phenolic compounds. *Food Sci. Technol.* **2008**, *41*, 652–659. [CrossRef]

22. Meredith, R.J. Introduction and fundamental concepts. In *Institution of Electrical Engineers, Engineers' Handbook of Industrial Microwave Heating*; IET: London, UK, 1998; pp. 1–16.

23. Fernandez, Y.; Arenillas, A.; Menendez, J.A. Microwave heating applied to pyrolysis. In *Advances in Induction and Microwave Heating of Mineral and Organic Materials*; Grundas, S., Ed.; IntechOpen: London, UK, 2011; pp. 723–751.

24. Haghi, A.K.; Amanifard, N. Analysis of heat and mass transfer during microwave drying of food products. *Braz. J. Chem. Eng.* **2008**, *25*, 491–501. [CrossRef]

25. Ingvarsson, M.K. Airflow and Energy Analysis in Geothermally Heated Conveyor Drying of Fishbone. MSc Thesis, Faculty of Industrial Engineering, Mechanical Engineering and Computer Science School of Engineering and Natural Sciences University of Iceland, Reykjavik, Iceland, June 2014.

26. Alamia, A.; Ström, H.; Thunman, A. Design of an integrated dryer and conveyor belt for woody biofuels. *Biomass Bioenergy* **2015**, *77*, 92–109. [CrossRef]

27. Tınmaz Köse, E.; Akyildiz, A.; Çelik, S.Ö.; Engin, E. *Treatment of Hydrocarbon Drilling Waste Sludge, Recovery and Recovery In The Construction Sector, Scientific Research Project, NKUBAP.06.GA.17.100 2017*; Tekirdağ Namık Kemal University: Tekirdağ, Turkey, December 2017.

28. Akcay, G. Drilling Fluid and Duties. 2013. Available online: http://geopazar.com/forum.asp?d23/Sondaj-Sivisi-ve-Gorevleri (accessed on 4 February 2019).

29. Çelen, S.; Aktaş, T.; Karabeyoğlu, S.S.; Akyıldız, A. Drying of prina using microwave energy and determination of appropriate thin layer drying model. *JOTAF* **2015**, *12*, 21–31.

30. Çelen, S.; Aktaş, T.; Karabeyoğlu, S.S.; Akyildiz, A. Drying Behaviour of Prina (Crude Olive Cake) Using Different Type of Dryers. *Dry Technol.* **2016**, *34*, 843–853. [CrossRef]

31. Tınmaz Köse, E.; Çelen, S.; Çelik, S.Ö.; Akın, G.; Akyıldız, A. Drying of drilling sludge: Conventional and microwave drying. *HJSE* **2019**, in press.

32. Huang, J.; Zhang, M.; Adhikari, B.; Yang, Z. Effect of microwave air spouted drying arranged in two and three-stages on the drying uniformity and quality of dehydrated carrot cubes. *J. Food Process. Eng.* **2016**, *177*, 80–89. [CrossRef]

Article

Effect of Temperature and Microwave Power Levels on Microwave Drying Kinetics of Zhaotong Lignite

Pengfei Zhao [1,2], Chenhui Liu [1,2,*], Wenwen Qu [3], Zhixiu He [1,2], Jiyun Gao [1,2], Lijuan Jia [1,2], Siping Ji [1,2] and Roger Ruan [4]

[1] Key Laboratory of Resource Clean Conversion in Ethnic Regions, Education Department of Yunnan Province, School of Chemistry and Environment, Yunnan Minzu University, Kunming 650500, China; Zhaoyan_0829@126.com (P.Z.); 18487168624@126.com (Z.H.); jiyungao89@163.com (J.G.); leegyerKM@163.com (L.J.); 17210154@163.com (S.J.)

[2] Key Laboratory of Comprehensive Utilization of Mineral Resources in Ethnic Regions, Yunnan Minzu University, Kunming 650500, China

[3] Faculty of Science, Kunming University of Science and Technology, Kunming 650500, China; qwwen77@163.com

[4] Center for Biorefining, Bioproducts and Biosystems Engineering Department, University of Minnesota, Saint Paul, MN 55101, USA; ruanx001@umn.edu

* Correspondence: liu-chenhui@hotmail.com; Tel.: +86-151-9873-8580

Received: 28 November 2018; Accepted: 25 January 2019; Published: 2 February 2019

Abstract: Microwave drying is a promising and effective way to drying and upgrading lignite. The influence of temperature (100–140 °C) and microwave power levels (500–800 W) on thin-layer drying characteristics of Zhaotong lignite under microwave irradiation were investigated. Fourteen thin-layer drying models were used to analyze the microwave drying process while six thin-layer drying models were used to analyze the hot-air drying process. The microwave drying processes at all temperature (100–140 °C) or low microwave power levels (500–700 W) exhibited four periods: a warm-up period, a short constant period, the first and second falling rate period, while one falling rate period was found during hot-air drying. The effective diffusion coefficient of lignite were calculated and it increases with increasing temperature and microwave power levels. During microwave drying, the two-term exponential model is the most suitable model for all applied conditions, while the Modified Page model is the most suitable model to describe the hot-air drying experiments. The apparent activation energy were determined from Arrhenius equation and the values for the first and second falling rate period are 3.349 and 20.808 kJ·mol^{-1} at different temperatures, while they are 13.455 and 19.580 W·g^{-1} at different microwave power levels. This implies the apparent activation energy is higher during the second falling rate period, which suggest that the dewatering of absorbed water is more difficult than capillary water. The value of apparent activation energy in hot-air drying is between the first and second falling rate period of microwave drying. Results indicate that microwave drying is more suitable to dewatering free water and capillary water of lignite.

Keywords: lignite; microwave drying kinetics; hot-air drying kinetics; effective diffusion coefficient; apparent activation energy

---

1. Introduction

Presently, with the consumption of energy demands increasing, the storage of high-rank coal has decreased quickly. Lignite is usually characterized with high water content [1], which results in low heat value, and higher fuel consumption and transportation cost [2]. However, lignite accounts for approximately 45% of the world's coal reserves, due to the advantages of lower mining cost, high reactivity, and low pollution impurities [3], it will be used more widely in the future. Thus, moisture removal is the first essential step to improve the quality of lignite by drying technologies in downstream utilization, such as pyrolysis, gasification, liquefaction, and combustion.

Various lignite dehydration technologies have been developed and researched by evaporation or non-evaporation methods [4]. Solar drying [5], steam-fluidized bed drying [6], and flue gas drum drying [7] are based on evaporation drying, while mechanical thermal expression [8,9] and hydrothermal dewatering [10,11] are based on non-evaporation drying. In traditional drying technologies, heat is transferred from the surface to the interior of the material by convection and conduction while the moisture transferred from the inside of the material to the surface. Most of thermal drying process are operated with combustion gas or superheated water vapor and the configuration of the drying reactor are complicated, which induces high costs of construction. In addition, traditional methods will lead to heating inhomogeneity, which is not beneficial for lignite upgrade. Among these dehydration technologies, microwave drying of low-rank coal is a very promising method due to its unique heating features.

Microwaves are electromagnetic waves with frequencies that range from 300 MHz to 300 GHz [12,13]. Microwave heating is a type of dielectric heating in which microwave energy is converted directly within material into thermal energy in the form of molecular friction or dielectric loss. It offers several advantages, such as non-contact heating, volumetric heating, selective heating, rapid heating. In microwave field, materials can be divided into insulators, conductors, and absorbers. Dipolar molecules in lignite, such as water, have a high dielectric constant and loss factor compared with dry lignite, can absorb microwave energy quickly and turn into thermal energy while the dry lignite particle maintain a low microwave absorbability [14]. Therefore, heat is transferred from the core to the surface of the lignite in microwave heating and the direction is identical with the moisture migration [15]. Consequently, the lignite can be dried quickly by microwave.

Microwave drying methods can be performed at lower temperatures, which can avoid surface overheating due to the removal of water [16]. Second, the moisture removal rate can be greatly promoted, as the mass transfer direction is identical with the thermal energy, which is generated by microwave energy. Third, moisture in the lignite can be heated through direct interaction between microwaves and moisture and a more uniform temperature distribution can be achieved due to volumetric heating [17]. Owing to these distinctive characteristics, numerous heating technologies based on microwaves have been developed to apply in various fields, such as the food processing industry [18], biological industry [15], agriculture industry [19], and mineral processing [20]. Therefore, it should be an effective drying method to upgrade lignite. In addition, microwave heating technology has been widely used in coal processing at lab and industrial scales. For example, in the pretreatment of lignite, microwaves can be used to dry lignite and improve its grinding characteristics, which are effected by the particle size and initial moisture of materials [21,22]. Microwave heating technology also has great potential for the pyrolysis and the production of coke from low-rank coal, which is inappropriate for traditional cooking plants [23,24].

Studies on drying kinetics and mathematical modeling of lignite during the drying process are essential for further understanding the drying mechanism. Researchers have conducted a great deal of work on temperature, particle size, thickness, and power levels of lignite. Zhu et al. [25] investigated the effect of coal particle size and microwave power level on the drying characteristics of lignite and derived that the apparent activation energy of the sample is 77.049 W/g. Li et al. [26] observed the removal of different form water in lignite and obtained that the effective diffusion coefficient are ranging from 0.371×10^{-8} to 1.672×10^{-8} $m^2 \cdot min^{-1}$ of MWC (raw lignite with molecular water) and from 0.509×10^{-8} to 3.317×10^{-8} $m^2 \cdot min^{-1}$ of RC (raw lignite with total water). The apparent activation energy of MWC and RC is 28.590 $kJ \cdot mol^{-1}$ and 24.250 $kJ \cdot mol^{-1}$, respectively. Fu et al. [12] evaluated the influence of additives on apparent activation energy and energy efficiency of lignite, which were increased with the addition of Na_2SO_4, Na_2CO_3 and coal fly ash of lignite. Fu et al. [27] also examined the microwave energy and temperature distribution of compressed lignite spheres and derived that the activation energy for particle sizes of 10 mm and 20 mm are 134.940 and 41.930 $W \cdot g^{-1}$, respectively.

Although some research has been accomplished on the drying behavior of lignite under different microwave power and temperatures. However, kinetics analysis in different microwave heating temperatures based on two falling rate periods and different microwave output levels are barely reported, especially in different microwave heating temperatures. Researchers have carried out a great deal of work on kinetics of temperature effects using conventional methods such as fluid bed dryer, hydrothermal dewatering and steam-fluidized bed dryer while the research on microwave drying lignite is still less. The present work was undertaken to explore the thin-layer drying kinetics and mathematical modeling of Zhaotong lignite at different temperatures and power levels. The effective diffusion coefficient and activation energy of lignite during the drying process were determined. The observation of this work can provide directions and support for deep processing and further utilization of lignite.

2. Experimental

2.1. Sample Preparation

This study used lignite from the Zhaotong region (Zhaotong, Yunnan Province, China), which is an important producer of lignite in China.

2.2. Experimental Apparatus and Procedure

A schematic of the experimental system is shown in Figure 1. The experiment was performed in a multimode microwave high-temp material treatment system [28], self-made by the Kunming University of Science and Technology (Kunming, China) (frequency: 2.45 GHz, maximum power output: 3000 W) and it can be operated at different power outputs. The microwave source consists of three Panasonic magnetrons (2M167B-M11, Panasonic Appliances Magnetron, Shanghai, China). The workstation was equipped with a fiber optical sensor (FOT-L-SD, Apollo Electronics, Shenzhen, China) with an accuracy of 1 °C to monitor the temperature information of the sample, and the temperature information was adjusted and displayed on the control panel through a PID control system (Kunming University of Science and Technology, Kunming, China) located on the microwave workstation. The workstation was modified by adding an electronic balance with an accuracy of 0.01 g (JJ-500, G&G Measurement Plant, Changshu, China), which was connected to a personal computer for continuously recording the weight change by a data acquisition system. The quartz crucible with a height of 60 mm and diameter of 40 mm was suspended from the balance by a quartz chain to contain the coal sample.

Before the microwave drying experiment, a 50 g sample was first put in the quartz crucible, then, the sample and the quartz crucible both placed in the center of the sample cavity and suspended from the balance by a quartz chain. Then, the microwave drying experiment started at different conditions through adjusting the buttons on the microwave workstation. Meanwhile, the data acquisition system recorded the mass information at 1 min intervals and the temperature measurements were carried out through a fiber optical sensor, which was very thin and it did not affect the measurement of mass change. Each experiment was finished when the sample mass no longer changed.

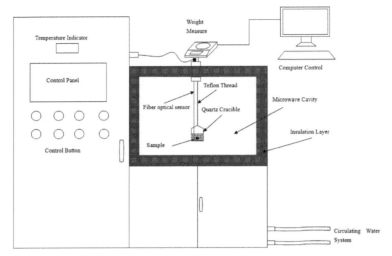

Figure 1. Schematic illustration of the microwave heating system.

When considering the effect of temperature, the microwave drying experiment was carried out under 100 °C, 120 °C, and 140 °C. To ensure temperature stability, the sample was periodically irradiated at a constant applied power (500 W). When considering the effect of microwave power levels, applied microwave power was 500 W, 600 W, 700 W, and 800 W, respectively, and the drying experiment was non-isothermal in these conditions. The drying experiment were repeated three times with similar results and the values of the relative deviations for mass and temperature were determined as ±1% and ±3%, respectively. Therefore, the average values were used for further study.

The hot-air drying experiments were carried out in an electric drying oven with forced convection (DHG-9075A, YIHENG, Shanghai, China). The equipment was driven by a 220 V voltage at 50 GHz. The temperature tested ranges of the cavity from 0–300 °C with an accuracy of 0.1 °C. The dimensions of hot-air drying chamber were 450 mm × 400 mm × 450 mm. In each experiment, a 50 g sample was put in the quartz crucible, the sample and the quartz crucible was measured by a digital balance with an accuracy of 0.01 g (JJ-500, G&G Measurement Plant, Changshu, China). The sample's weight was measured every 10 min during hot air drying. When considering the effect of temperature, the hot-air drying experiments were carried out under 100 °C, 120 °C, and 140 °C. Each experiment was finished when the sample mass did not change.

2.3. Mathematical Modeling

To find the suitable fit model, the moisture ratio data curves obtained from drying experiments at different conditions were fitted by different mathematical models, which are shown in Table 1.

In all experiments, the moisture value (M), drying rate (DR), and moisture ratio (MR) of coal samples were calculated by using the following equations:

$$M = \frac{W_t - W_{d,s}}{W_{d,s}} \tag{1}$$

$$DR = \frac{M_t - M_{t+dt}}{dt} \tag{2}$$

$$MR = \frac{M_t - M_e}{M_0 - M_e} \tag{3}$$

where M is the moisture (g/(g db)), W_t (g) is the mass of sample at t, $W_{d,s}$ is the dry coal mass (g), DR is the drying rate (g/(g db min)), M_t and M_{t+dt} are the moisture content at t and $t + dt$ (g/(g db)), respectively, MR is the moisture ratio, M_0 is the initial water content (g/(g db)), and M_e is the moisture content at the end of the drying experiment (g/(g db)), which can be assumed to be zero for microwave drying. Therefore, the mathematical expression of MR was written as Equation (4):

$$MR = \frac{M_t}{M_0} \tag{4}$$

Table 1. Mathematical thin-layer drying models. Reproduced with permission from Zhu, J.-F. et al., Fuel Processing Technology; published by Elsevier [25].

Number	Drying Models	Equation
1	Page	$exp(-kt^n)$ [29,30]
2	Modified Page	$exp(-(kt)^n)$ [31]
3	Modified Page equation-II	$a\, exp(-k(t/L_2)^n)$ [32]
4	Simplified Fick's diffusion	$a\, exp(-c(t/L_2))$ [32]
5	Two-term	$a\, exp(-k_0 t) + b\, exp(-k_1 t)$ [33,34]
6	Two-term exponential	$a\, exp(-kt) + (1-a)\, exp(-kat)$ [35]
7	Newton	$exp(-kt)$ [36–38]
8	Henderson and Pabis	$a\, exp(-kt)$ [39,40]
9	Modified Henderson and Pabis	$a\, exp(-kt) + b\, exp(-gt) + c\, exp(-ht)$ [41]
10	Logarithmic	$a\, exp(-kt) + c$ [42]
11	Wang and Singh	$1 + at + bt^2$ [43]
12	Diffusion approach	$a\, exp(-kt) + (1-a)\, exp(-kbt)$ [44]
13	Verma	$a\, exp(-kt) + (1-a)\, exp(-gt)$ [45]
14	Midilli–Kucuk	$exp(-kt^n) + bt$ [46]

3. Results and Discussion

3.1. Proximate Analysis of Raw Lignite

This study used lignite from the Zhaotong region and the proximate analysis of raw lignite is shown in Table 2.

Table 2. Proximate analysis of raw lignite.

Lignite	M_{ad}	A_{ad}	V_{ad}	FC_{ad}
wt. (%)	35.61	24.49	26.29	13.59

M_{ad}, A_{ad}, V_{ad}, and FC_{ad} refer to the moisture, ash, volatile, and fixed carbon content on an air-dried basis, respectively.

3.2. The Effect of Temperature during Microwave Drying

The changes in sample mass, moisture ratio, drying rate versus time and drying rate versus moisture ratio of the Zhaotong lignite are shown in Figure 2a–d.

From Figure 2a,b, temperature levels have a significant effect on mass change and drying time. The sample mass decrease rapidly within 300 s and drying time decreases with the increase in temperature levels. As shown from Figure 2b, the drying time for the raw lignite is 1260 s at 100 °C, while it was 900 s and 660 s as the temperature rose to 120 °C and 140 °C.The drying time decreases by about 29% and 48%, respectively. The boiling point of water is 100 °C, and moisture migration of lignite is easier as the temperature increases from 100 °C to 120 °C and 140 °C. Therefore, a higher temperature can lead to the decline of the required microwave drying time.

A turning point, also called the maximum drying rate point, is the demarcation point of the increasing period and the falling rate period. At the turning point, with the migration of a large amount of bulk water from the raw lignite, there is no moisture at the surface due to the insufficient supply of bulk water from the capillaries [47]. As shown in Figure 2c, the drying rate of all samples reach the maximum rate point in about 100 s, which can be attributed to the fact that the thermal energy generated by microwave energy increase with increasing temperature. In addition, the drying rate curves present several different stages between 100–140 °C: a very brief warm-up period (A), a short constant rate period (B), and two obviously different falling rate periods (refer to the first falling rate (C) and the second falling rate (D)).

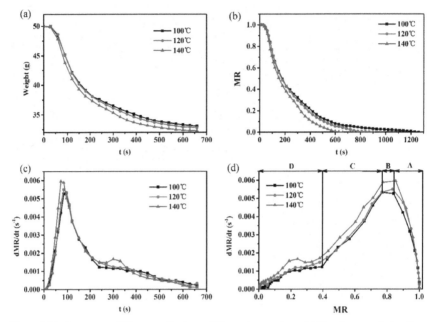

Figure 2. Drying curves of Zhaotong lignite at different temperature. (**a**) Mass loss vs. drying time; (**b**) moisture ratio vs. drying time; (**c**) drying rate vs. drying time; and (**d**) drying rate vs. moisture ratio.

During the warm-up period, mostly bulk water evaporates, resulting in massive mass loss and, therefore, the drying rate increases significantly. This is due to the high dielectric constant and loss factor of the water [26]. The drying rate is a short constant in the (B) period, which could be attributed to the sufficient supply of bulk water and the balance between the water evaporation energy and the thermal energy generated by microwave energy [12]. However, the constant rate period was detected at all different temperature drying experiment which can be ascribe to the temperature of the sample. Although the maximum temperature studied in this paper is 140 °C, it is still lower than the temperature at different power levels in other research. Zhu et al. [25] revealed that the final temperature of lignite could reach 207 °C when 700 W was applied to the sample. Due to a great deal of bulk water being removed during the warm-up period or the constant rate period, the drying rate became smaller, and that is the falling rate period. In addition, two obviously different periods can be detected in the falling rate period refer to the first falling rate (C) and the second falling rate (D).

As mentioned above, a great deal of bulk water has been removed in the warm-up period or the constant rate period. Therefore, the mass loss is mainly ascribed to the removal of capillary water in the first falling rate period which has lower dielectric constant than the bulk water. However, the water molecule migration force are increase due to the capillary water tightly bound to the solid particles. Therefore the drying rate tends to decrease in the first falling rate period.

Compared to the first falling rate period, the absorbed water is being removed in the second falling rate period, and the drying rate decreases slightly, which can be attributed to the amount of the absorbed water being relatively less and having a lower dielectric loss factor than the capillary water. In addition, the desorption of absorbed water, which is in the state of multilayer and monolayer adsorption, needs to break down the stronger hydrogen bonds [26], therefore, a further reduction of the drying rate can be detected in the second falling rate period.

3.3. The Effect of Microwave Power Levels during Microwave Drying

Temperature variations, drying curves, and drying rate curves about microwave output power levels were shown in Figure 3a–d. The drying time decreases significantly and the drying rate increases sharply as the microwave power level increases from 500 W to 600 W, 700 W, and 800 W, which can be attributed to the fact that the electromagnetic intensity increases simultaneously with the increase in drying power level. A great deal of heat energy is generated in a rapidly alternating electric field.

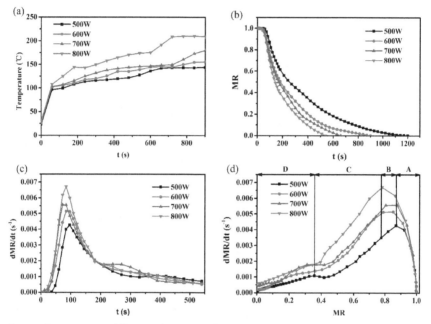

Figure 3. Drying curves of Zhaotong lignite at different microwave power levels. (**a**) Temperature vs. drying time; (**b**) moisture ratio vs. drying time; (**c**) drying rate vs. drying time; and (**d**) drying rate vs. moisture ratio.

As can be observed in Figure 3b, the microwave drying time of raw lignite was 1200 s at 500 W, whereas it was only 900 s, 660 s, and 540 s with the microwave power level ascending to 600 W, 700 W, and 800 W. Results show that microwave drying can be an effective and potential ways to upgrade raw lignite for its further utilization. As shown in Figure 3c, the drying rate increases sharply within 100 s and reaches its maximum value rapidly. The maximum drying rate of all samples increased from 0.004 to 0.007 g/g·s^{-1} with increasing power levels. In this process, two periods are detected in the microwave drying experiment, which is referred to a warm-up period within 60 s and a constant rate period between 60 s and 120 s. The mass change in these two periods was mainly ascribed to the evaporation of bulk water, which mainly exists in the surface of the sample. When the applied microwave power level is 800 W, an obviously constant rate period appears, which is similar to the former researchers' experimental results. Song et al. [48] found that the constant rate period were discovered under 700 W, while it disappeared at 800 W. This can be explained by a great deal of heat energy generation and higher pressure difference at microwave power levels beyond 700 W, leading to the increasing drying rate and the final temperature of lignite reaching 181 °C, as can be observed in Figure 3a.

Beyond the turning point, two falling rate periods were observed, which are similar with the drying rate curves regarding temperature. However, according to the drying curves in Figure 3d, the changes of drying rate are more obvious between the two falling rate periods compared to the experiments on temperature, which can be related to the larger amount of thermal energy converted from microwaves. During the first falling rate period, the drying rate decreases rapidly. In addition, due to the capillary water migration by molecular diffusion, the resistance increase sharply with the decrease of moisture content. As seen from Figure 3d, the drying rate decrease further in the second falling rate period. During this period, the mass loss mainly attributed to the remove of absorbed water. Due to the existence of hydrophilic oxygen-containing groups in the lignite, the evaporation resistance of moisture is greater than capillary water. Therefore, the drying rate decreases further in this period.

3.4. The Effect of Temperature during Hot-Air Drying

Drying curves and drying rate curves of lignite at different temperature by hot-air drying method was shown in Figure 4a,b. As observed in Figure 4a, the drying time of lignite decrease with increasing temperature due to the increasing drying force. For example, when the drying temperature increases from 100 °C to 120 °C or 140 °C, drying time decreases from 380 min to 300 min and 210 min, decreasing by 27% and 45%, respectively. However, compared with microwave drying, under the same drying conditions, the drying time only needs 1260 s, 900 s and 660 s from 100 °C to 120 °C and 140 °C, respectively.

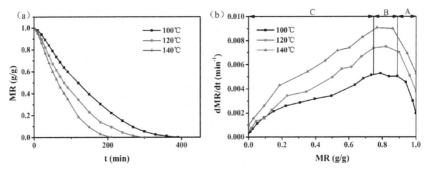

Figure 4. Drying curves of Zhaotong lignite at different temperature by hot-air drying method. (a) Moisture ratio vs. drying time; (b) drying rate vs. moisture ratio.

As seen in Figure 4b, the variation of drying rate of lignite at different temperatures can be roughly divided into three stages: a warm up period (A), a short constant rate period (B), and a falling rate period (C). In the warm up period, the drying rate increase monotonously and reach its maximum in about 40 min at 100 °C and 120 °C, while it is about 30 min at 140 °C. Beyond the maximum drying rate point, the drying rate remains constant for a short time, about 10–30 min. The constant rate period sustain longer at low temperature conditions. The mass change in these two periods was mainly ascribed to the evaporation of bulk water, which mainly exists in the surface of the sample. Compared with microwave drying, two obviously different falling rate periods were not found, only one falling rate period was observed after the constant rate period, which could be ascribed to the drying characteristics of hot-air drying. During the hot-air drying, the heat energy transformed from the surface to the interior of lignite, whereas moisture migrates in the opposite direction. This means that the moisture does not migrate smoothly. The comparisons of the drying characteristics of lignite between microwave drying and hot-air drying indicate that microwave drying has great advantages in drying time and rate.

3.5. Kinetics Modeling of Microwave Drying

In order to obtain drying kinetics information, 14 thin-layer drying models in Table 1 were fitted for all drying experiment. In addition, the coefficient of determination (R^2), which was one of the main parameter to evaluate the most suitable model, the reduced chi-square (χ^2), the residual sum of square (RSS) and the F-value were used to find the best model for experimental data [49]. The better goodness of fit were determined by higher values of R^2 and F-value while lower values of χ^2 and RSS.

The fitted results for all drying conditions are presented in Tables 3 and 4. Considering the effect of temperature and power level, Modified Page, modified Page equationII, and two-term exponential models show good results for all experimental data. The mean values of R^2, RSS, χ^2, and F-value for the Modified Page model were 0.991, 0.012, 1.011×10^{-3}, and 1684.663, while the results are 0.991, 0.023, 1.032×10^{-3}, and 797.817 for the modified Page equationII and 0.993, 0.011, 8.231×10^{-4}, and 1837.998 for the two-term exponential model. Due to the higher values of R^2 and F-value while lower values of χ^2 and RSS, the two-term exponential is the best model for all experimental data. Therefore, the two-term exponential model is the most suitable model to describe the microwave drying experiments.

Table 3. Evaluated results of mathematical thin-layer drying models at different temperatures.

	T (°C)	Coefficients	R^2	RSS	χ^2	F-Value
Diffusion approach	100	k = 0.168, a = -2.477×10^6, b = 1	0.987	0.021	1.000×10^{-3}	880.066
	120	k = 0.244, a = 1, b = 1	0.975	0.035	3.000×10^{-3}	349.727
	140	k = 0.286, a = 1, b = 1	0.964	0.040	4.000×10^{-3}	189.560
Henderson and Pabis	100	k = 0.24173, a = 1.065	0.991	0.016	1.000×10^{-3}	1799.371
	120	k = 0.26296, a = 1.084	0.984	0.024	2.000×10^{-3}	836.923
	140	k = 0.30745, a = 1.085	0.976	0.030	3.000×10^{-3}	434.304
Midilli-Kucuk	100	k = -14.706, a = 4.062×10^{-7}, b = -0.008, n = -0.047	0.363	1.026	5.700×10^{-2}	8.543
	120	k = -11.318, a = 1.202×10^{-5}, b = -0.017, n = -0.559	0.227	1.012	8.400×10^{-2}	5.585
	140	k = -0.477, a = 0.609, b = -0.064, n = -3.497×10^6	-0.058	1.041	1.300×10^{-2}	2.983
Modified Henderdon and Pabis	100	k = 0.242, a = 0.355, b = 0.355, c = 0.355	0.989	0.016	1.000×10^{-3}	479.832
	120	k = 0.263, a = 0.361, b = 0.361, c = 0.361	0.978	0.024	2.000×10^{-3}	199.267
	140	k = 0.307, a = 0.362, b = 0.362, c = 0.362	0.960	0.030	5.000×10^{-3}	86.861
Modified Page	100	k = 0.222, n = 1.164	0.992	0.014	7.031×10^{-4}	2106.905
	120	k = 0.235, n = 1.278	0.992	0.012	8.832×10^{-4}	1633.806
	140	k = 0.274, n = 1.372	0.992	0.009	9.274×10^{-4}	1392.609
Modified Page equationII	100	k = 7.967, a = 1.036, L = 5.264, n = 1.118	0.992	0.013	6.952×10^{-4}	1065.687
	120	k = 4.745, a = 1.032, L = 3.819, n = 1.231	0.992	0.011	9.242×10^{-4}	780.449
	140	k = 0.548, a = 1.022, L = 1.511, n = 1.335	0.991	0.009	1.000×10^{-3}	595.534
Newton	100	k = 0.228	0.988	0.023	1.120×10^{-3}	2643.955
	120	k = 0.244	0.978	0.035	2.000×10^{-3}	1210.594
	140	k = 0.286	0.970	0.040	4.000×10^{-3}	695.052
Page	100	k = 0.173, n = 1.165	0.988	0.023	1.000×10^{-3}	2643.955
	120	k = 0.157, n = 1.278	0.978	0.035	2.000×10^{-3}	1210.594
	140	k = 0.286, n = 1.342	0.970	0.040	4.000×10^{-3}	695.052
Simplified_Ficks diffusion	100	a = 1.065, c = 1.519, L = 2.507	0.990	0.016	8.654×10^{-4}	1139.602
	120	a = 1.084, c = 1.135, L = 2.077	0.983	0.024	2.000×10^{-3}	518.096
	140	a = 1.085, c = 0.661, L = 1.466	0.973	0.030	3.000×10^{-3}	260.583
Two-term	100	a = 0.532, b = 0.532, k_0 = 0.242, k_1 = 0.242	0.990	0.016	9.132×10^{-4}	809.717
	120	a = 0.542, b = 0.542, k_0 = 0.263, k_1 = 0.263	0.982	0.024	2.000×10^{-3}	358.681
	140	a = 0.543, b = 0.543, k_0 = 0.307, k_1 = 0.307	0.970	0.030	4.000×10^{-3}	173.722
Two-term exponential	100	k = 0.310, a = 1.747	0.992	0.014	7.213×10^{-4}	2052.358
	120	k = 0.362, a = 1.909	0.993	0.011	7.981×10^{-4}	1808.309
	140	k = 0.443, a = 0.068	0.99375	0.008	7.692×10^{-4}	1680.382

Table 3. *Cont.*

	T (°C)	Coefficients	R^2	RSS	χ^2	F-Value
Verma	100	k = 0.267, a = 1.180, g = 3496.365	0.997	0.005	2.673×10^{-4}	3706.411
	120	k = 0.302, a = 1.252, g = 2.31 × 10⁷	0.997	0.004	2.784×10^{-4}	3465.462
	140	k = 0.366, a = 1.310, g = 1066.695	0.996	0.004	4.901×10^{-4}	1761.785
Wang and singh	100	a = −0.140, b = 0.005	0.937	0.113	6.000×10^{-3}	252.193
	120	a = −0.169, b = 0.007	0.979	0.032	2.000×10^{-3}	620.447
	140	a = −0.205, b = 0.011	0.986	0.017	2.000×10^{-3}	749.792
Logarithmic	100	k = 0.239, a = 1.067, c = −0.003	0.990	0.016	8.611×10^{-4}	1145.754
	120	k = 0.233, a = 1.114, c = −0.047	0.987	0.018	1.000×10^{-3}	677.532
	140	k = 0.243, a = 1.162, c = −0.103	0.985	0.017	2.000×10^{-3}	450.334

Table 4. Evaluated results of mathematical thin-layer drying models at different microwave power levels.

Model	W	Coefficients	R^2	RSS	χ^2	F-Value
Diffusion approach	500	k = 0.166, a = 1, b = 1	0.983	0.031	$2.000 \times 10^{-3.}$	754.788
	600	k = 0.232, a = 1.041 × 10¹², b = 1	0.975	0.036	3.000×10^{-3}	363.305
	700	k = 0.12721, a = 1.578 × 10¹³, b = 1	0.980	0.021	3.000×10^{-3}	384.447
	800	k = 0.30273, a = 1, b = 1	0.948	0.047	7.000×10^{-3}	121.368
Henderson and Pabis	500	k = 0.178, a = 1.080	0.990	0.019	9.942×10^{-4}	1938.079
	600	k = 0.249, a = 1.090	0.985	0.023	2.000×10^{-3}	894.744
	700	k = 0.282, a = 1.090	0.977	0.028	3.000×10^{-3}	489.825
	800	k = 0.328, a = 1.090	0.966	0.036	4.400×10^{-2}	278.231
Midilli-Kucuk	500	k = −9.441, a = 8.219 × 10⁻⁵, b = −0.017, n = −0.048	0.399	1.015	6.000×10^{-2}	11.960
	600	k = −10.555, a = 2.609 × 10⁻⁵, b = −0.017, n = −0.056	0.227	1.012	8.400×10^{-2}	5.968
	700	k = −10.562, a = 2.532 × 10⁻⁵, b = −0.027, n = −0.053	0.038	1.004	0.126	3.526
	800	k = −0.189, k = 0.178, a = 0.358, b = −0.395, n = 0.867	0.969	0.024	4.000×10^{-3}	154.053
Modified Henderdon and Pabis	500	b = 0.358, c = 0.358	0.987	0.019	1.000×10^{-3}	510.021
	600	k = 0.249, a = 0.362, b = 0.362, c = 0.362	0.978	0.023	2.000×10^{-3}	213.034
	700	k = 0.328, a = 0.363, b = 0.363, c = 0.363	0.961	0.028	5.000×10^{-3}	97.965
	800	b = 0.363, c = 0.363 k = 0.363, a = 0.363,	0.932	0.036	9.000×10^{-3}	46.372
Modified Page	500	k = 0.162, n = 1.193	0.993	0.013	6.831×10^{-4}	2825.111
	600	k = 0.223, n = 1.273	0.992	0.012	8.879×10^{-4}	1696.047
	700	k = 0.251, n = 1.357	0.992	0.010	9.858×10^{-4}	1402.093
	800	k = 0.292, n = 1.418	0.987	0.014	2.000×10^{-3}	736.068
Modified Page equation-II	500	k = 0.376, a = 1.031, n = 1.148, L = 1.598	0.993	0.012	6.870×10^{-4}	1405.019
	600	k = 4.602, a = 1.034, n = 1.223, L = 3.886	0.992	0.011	9.182×10^{-4}	820.476
	700	k = 4.399, a = 1.027, n = 1.312, L = 3.463	0.991	0.090	1.000×10^{-3}	617.745
	800	k = 7.435, a = 1.030, n = 1.368, L = 3.798	0.984	0.012	2.000×10^{-3}	299.810

Table 4. *Cont.*

Model	W	Coefficients	R^2	RSS	χ^2	F-Value
Newton	500	k = 0.166	0.985	0.031	1.000×10^{-3}	2515.960
	600	k = 0.231	0.978	0.036	2.000×10^{-3}	1257.561
	700	k = 0.261	0.970	0.040	4.000×10^{-3}	748.017
	800	k = 0.303	0.960	0.047	5.000×10^{-3}	468.135
Page	500	k = 0.114, n = 1.193	0.993	0.013	6.831×10^{-4}	2825.109
	600	k = 0.231, n = 1.274	0.992	0.012	8.879×10^{-4}	1696.032
	700	k = 0.154, n = 1.357	0.992	0.010	9.858×10^{-4}	1402.087
	800	k = 0.174, n = 1.419	0.987	0.014	2.000×10^{-3}	736.064
Simplified Ficks diffusion	500	a = 1.076, c = 6.563, L = 6.066	0.989	0.019	1.000×10^{-3}	1224.052
	600	a = 1.086, c = 1.285, L = 2.271	0.983	0.023	2.000×10^{-3}	553.889
	700	a = 1.089, c = 0.849, L = 1.735	0.974	0.028	3.000×10^{-3}	2993.895
	800	a = 1.091, c = 0.574, L = 1.323	0.960	0.036	5.000×10^{-3}	162.302
Two term	500	a = 0.538, b = 0.538, k_0 = 0.178, k_1 = 0.178	0.989	0.019	1.000×10^{-3}	867.035
	600	a = 0.543, b = 0.543, k_0 = 0.249, k_1 = 0.249	0.982	0.023	2.000×10^{-3}	383.461
	700	a = 0.544, b = 0.544, k_0 = 0.282, k_1 = 0.282	0.971	0.028	4.000×10^{-3}	195.930
	800	a = 0.545, b = 0.545, k_0 = 0.328, k_1 = 0.328	0.955	0.036	6.000×10^{-3}	104.337
Two–term exponential	500	a = 1.751, k = 0.226	0.993	0.014	7.448×10^{-4}	2590.107
	600	a = 1.900, k = 0.341	0.993	0.011	8.102×10^{-4}	1859.288
	700	a = 1.988, k = 0.405	0.994	0.008	7.776×10^{-4}	1778.736
	800	a = 2.080, k = 0.494	0.991	0.009	1.140×10^{-3}	1096.804
Verma	500	k = 0.191, a = 1.157, g = 0.191	0.997	0.007	3.999×10^{-4}	3221.211
	600	k = 0.284, a = 1.242, g = 55.727	0.998	0.003	2.642×10^{-4}	3836.985
	700	k = 0.332, a = 1.292, g = 224.580	0.997	0.003	3.578×10^{-4}	2581.325
	800	k = 0.302, a = –0.301, g = 0.303	0.948	0.047	7.000×10^{-3}	121.368
Wang and Singh	500	a = –0.118, b = 0.004	0.984	0.031	2.000×10^{-3}	1189.696
	600	a = –0.163, b = 0.007	0.981	0.029	2.000×10^{-3}	717.017
	700	a = –0.191, b = 0.009	0.984	0.019	2.000×10^{-3}	730.583
	800	a = –0.222, b = 0.013	0.977	0.024	3.000×10^{-3}	414.547
Logarithmic	500	a = 1.107, k = 0.155, c = –0.054	0.993	0.012	6.774×10^{-4}	1899.599
	600	a = 1.117, k = 0.220, c = –0.049	0.987	0.018	1.000×10^{-3}	717.731
	700	a = 1.173, k = 0.221, c = –0.111	0.984	0.017	2.000×10^{-3}	482.027
	800	a = 1.207, k = 0.244, c = –0.144	0.975	0.023	3.000×10^{-3}	253.729

3.6. Kinetics Modeling of Hot-Air Drying

In order to obtain drying kinetic information in the falling rate period during the hot-air drying, the page model, Modified Page model, Newton model, logarithmic model, Henderson and Pabis, and Wang and Singh models were used to fit the experiment results. The fitted results for all drying conditions are presented in Table 5. Similar to the analytical methods used previously, the better goodness of fit was determined by higher values of R^2 and F-value while having lower values of χ^2 and RSS.

The fitted results for all drying conditions are presented in Table 5. Considering the effect of temperature, the Page model, Modified Page model, and Wang and Singh model show good results for all experimental data. The mean values of R^2, RSS, χ^2, and F-value for the modified Page model are 0.998, 0.004, 0.002, and 11,697.960, while being 0.998, 0.004, 2.62×10^{-3}, and 11,688.314 for the Page model and 0.998, 0.004, 2.820×10^{-4}, 10,634.21 for Wang and Singh model. Due to the higher values of R^2 and F-value while lower values of χ^2 and RSS, the Modified Page model is the best model for all experimental data. Therefore, the Modified Page model is the most suitable model to describe the hot-air drying experiments.

Table 5. Evaluated results of mathematical thin-layer drying models at different temperatures.

	T (°C)	Coefficients	R^2	RSS	χ^2	F-Value
Page	100	k = 0.001, n = 1.351	0.997	0.006	3.381×10^{-4}	10,807.829
	120	k = 0.002, n = 1.282	0.998	0.002	1.982×10^{-4}	14,537.140
	140	k = 0.002, n = 1.374	0.998	0.003	2.504×10^{-4}	9719.974
Modified Page	100	k = 0.007, n = 1.354	0.997	0.006	1.000×10^{-3}	10,814.961
	120	k = 0.009, n = 1.284	0.998	0.003	2.000×10^{-3}	14,540.871
	140	k = 0.012, n = 1.379	0.998	0.003	3.000×10^{-3}	9738.043
Newton	100	k = 0.007	0.971	0.071	4.000×10^{-3}	1939.489
	120	k = 0.009	0.980	0.037	2.000×10^{-3}	2448.516
	140	k = 0.012	0.969	0.045	3.000×10^{-3}	1407.829
Logarithmic	100	a = 0.563, k = −1223.565, c = 0.437	−1.859	6.313	0.371	0.898
	120	a = 0.590, k = −1245.021, c = 0.409	−1.853	4.766	0.340	0.979
	140	a = 0.586, k = −1202.048, c = 0.414	−2.125	3.871	0.352	0.947
Henderson and Pabis	100	a = 1.089, k = 0.007	0.982	0.041	2.000×10^{-3}	1580.406
	120	a = 1.074, k = 0.009	0.988	0.022	1.000×10^{-3}	1961.657
	140	a = 1.079, k = 0.013	0.978	0.029	2.000×10^{-3}	978.989
Wang and Singh	100	a = −0.005, b = 5.997×10^{-6}	0.998	0.005	2.791×10^{-4}	13,093.487
	120	a = −0.006, b = 1.235×10^{-5}	0.998	0.004	2.751×10^{-4}	10,472.483
	140	a = −0.009, b = 2.012×10^{-5}	0.997	0.004	2.919×10^{-4}	8336.658

3.7. Effective Diffusion Coefficient and Activation Energy

To further analyze the drying behavior of lignite in whole falling rate period, moisture of the lignite was removed from the internal to the external by diffusion, an effective diffusion coefficient could be obtained by Fick's second law under specific conditions [50]. As the diffusion coefficient demonstrate the mass transfer rate during microwave drying experiment, it could be used to indicate how well moisture was removed per unit time [22]. Based on the assumptions of moisture transport via diffusion, negligible shrinkage, constant coefficient and temperature, the following analytically derived equation could be used to calculate the diffusion coefficient:

$$\ln MR = \ln \frac{8}{\pi^2} - \frac{\pi^2 D_{eff}}{L^2} t \tag{5}$$

where D_{eff} ($m^2 \cdot s^{-1}$) is the effective diffusion coefficient; MR is the moisture ratio of lignite; L is the thickness of the thin-layer, m; and t is the drying time, s. The effective diffusion coefficient under specific conditions can be determined by plotting $\ln MR$ versus t.

Based on previous discussions, the whole falling rate period of microwave drying was distinguished into the first falling rate period and the second falling rate period, which could further determine the drying kinetics of lignite in the whole falling rate stage. However, during hot-air drying, only one falling rate period was found. Figure 5 demonstrates the linear fitting between $\ln MR$ and t from Equation (5) for the thin-layer in the first falling rate period and the second falling rate period at the experimental temperature of 100 °C. The effective diffusion coefficient of lignite could be determined according to the slope of the fitted lines and the results are presented in Tables 6–8 at different conditions.

The effective diffusion coefficient increased gradually with the increasing of temperature or microwave power levels in both periods. With the increase of temperature, the effective diffusion coefficient of the lignite increase from 7.081×10^{-7} to 7.871×10^{-7} $m^2 \cdot s^{-1}$ during the first falling rate period. In the second falling rate period, it vary from 6.511×10^{-7} to 1.189×10^{-6} $m^2 \cdot s^{-1}$. The effective diffusion coefficient of the lignite increase from 1.881×10^{-8} to 3.186×10^{-8} $m^2 \cdot s^{-1}$ during the hot-air drying. This means that increasing temperature helps the migration of moisture due to the drying force of moisture increase with increasing temperature. However, the effective diffusion coefficient during microwave drying is higher than hot-air drying whether in the first falling rate period or the second falling rate period, which could be ascribed to the different drying mechanism. Similarly, with the increase of microwave power level, the effective diffusion coefficient of the lignite increase from 6.247×10^{-9} to 1.093×10^{-8} m$^2 \cdot$s^{-1} during the first falling rate period. It varies from 4.696×10^{-9} to 1.008×10^{-8} m$^2 \cdot$s^{-1} during the second falling rate period. The temperature of lignite increase with the increase of microwave power levels. Consequently, the drying force increases gradually. Similar results were reported by Fu et al. [12] at the microwave power of 119–700 W. An interesting phenomenon shows that the effective diffusion coefficient at different temperatures are higher than that at different power levels.

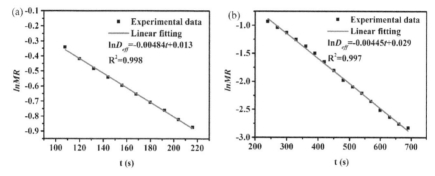

Figure 5. Plot of ln*MR* versus t of lignite at 100 °C. (**a**) 1st falling rate period; (**b**) 2nd falling rate period.

Table 6. Effective diffusion coefficient of lignite at different temperatures during microwave drying.

T (°C)	1st Falling Rate		2nd Falling Rate	
	D_{eff} (m$^2 \cdot$s^{-1})	R^2	D_{eff} (m$^2 \cdot$s^{-1})	R^2
100	7.081×10^{-7}	0.998	6.511×10^{-7}	0.997
120	7.213×10^{-7}	0.994	7.959×10^{-7}	0.997
140	7.871×10^{-7}	0.997	1.189×10^{-6}	0.998

Table 7. Effective diffusion coefficient of lignite at different microwave power levels during microwave drying.

P (W)	1st Falling Rate		2nd Falling Rate	
	D_{eff} (m$^2 \cdot$s^{-1})	R^2	D_{eff} (m$^2 \cdot$s^{-1})	R^2
500	6.247×10^{-9}	0.996	4.696×10^{-9}	0.999
600	8.120×10^{-9}	0.993	7.608×10^{-9}	0.999
700	8.325×10^{-9}	0.993	8.354×10^{-9}	0.997
800	1.093×10^{-8}	0.995	1.008×10^{-8}	0.990

Table 8. Effective diffusion coefficient of lignite at different temperatures during hot-air drying.

T (°C)	Falling Rate Period	
	D_{eff} (m$^2 \cdot$s^{-1})	R^2
100	1.881×10^{-8}	0.991
200	2.948×10^{-8}	0.991
300	3.186×10^{-8}	0.998

Apparent activation energy was determined by using the Arrhenius equation [51]:

$$D_{eff} = D_0 \exp\left(-\frac{E_a}{RT}\right) \qquad (6)$$

where D_0, E_a, T, and R are the diffusion factor ($m^2 \cdot s^{-1}$), the apparent activation energy, and the temperature of lignite (K) and the gas constant, respectively.

Equation (6) can be linearized as:

$$\ln D_{eff} = \ln D_0 - \frac{E_a}{RT} \qquad (7)$$

E_a and D_0 can be evaluated by plotting $\ln D_{eff}$ versus $1/T$. Due to the microwave drying process under different microwave power levels is not an isothermal process, the activation energy can be obtained by a modified Arrhenius equation:

$$D_{eff} = D_0 \exp\left(-\frac{E_a \times m}{p}\right) \qquad (8)$$

where m and P are the mass of sample (g) and the microwave power levels, respectively.

Equation (7) can be linearized as:

$$\ln D_{eff} = \ln D_0 - \frac{E_a \times m}{p} \qquad (9)$$

E_a and D_0 can be evaluated by plotting $\ln D_{eff}$ versus m/P.

The plots of $\ln D_{eff}$ versus m/P and the fitted line are presented in Figure 6, from which the E_a in the first falling rate period and second falling rate period could be determined. The results of microwave drying are presented in Tables 9 and 10, while the results of hot-air drying are presented in Table 11.

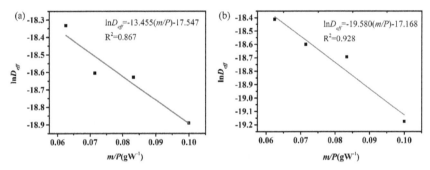

Figure 6. Plot of $\ln D_{eff}$ versus m/P of lignite. (**a**) 1st falling rate period; (**b**) 2nd falling rate period.

Table 9. Activation energy of lignite at different temperatures during microwave drying.

Condition	1st Falling Rate			2nd Falling Rate		
	E_a (kJ·mol^{-1})	D_0 ($m^2 \cdot s^{-1}$)	R^2	E_a (kJ·mol^{-1})	D_0 ($m^2 \cdot s^{-1}$)	R^2
T	3.349	2.060×10^{-6}	0.712	20.808	5.091×10^{-4}	0.879

Table 10. Activation energy of lignite at different microwave power levels during microwave drying.

Condition	1st Falling Rate			2nd Falling Rate		
	E_a (W·g^{-1})	D_0 ($m^2 \cdot s^{-1}$)	R^2	E_a (W·g^{-1})	D_0 ($m^2 \cdot s^{-1}$)	R^2
W	13.455	2.396×10^{-8}	0.867	19.580	3.500×10^{-8}	0.928

Table 11. Activation energy of lignite at different temperatures during hot-air drying.

Condition	Falling Rate Period		
	E_a (kJ·mol^{-1})	D_0 (m^2·s^{-1})	R^2
T	17.078	4.883×10^{-6}	0.756

During microwave drying, the values of apparent activation energy for the first and second falling rate periods at different temperatures are 3.349 and 20.808 kJ·mol^{-1}, respectively, and the values of diffusion factors are 2.060×10^{-6} and 5.091×10^{-4} m^2·s^{-1}. Similarly, the values of apparent activation energy at different microwave power levels are 13.455 and 19.580 W·g^{-1}, respectively. The values of diffusion factors are 2.396×10^{-8} and 3.500×10^{-8} m^2·s^{-1}. The apparent activation energy of the second falling rate period is higher than that of the first falling rate period in all microwave drying conditions. In other words, the removal of moisture is easier during the first falling rate period. During the first falling rate period, the mass loss can be mainly attributed to the removal of capillary water compared to absorbed water during the second falling rate period. Capillary water, which exists in the pore channels of lignite, was removed through overcoming the Van der Waals forces and hydrogen bond resistance, which exists among the water molecules [26]. However, the amount of absorbed water is relatively less and it is tightly bounded to the solid particles. In addition, there are a great deal of hydrophilic oxygen-containing groups in the lignite. Therefore, the apparent activation energy is higher during the second falling rate period [26].

In hot-air drying, the value of apparent activation energy for the falling rate period at different temperatures is 17.078 kJ·mol^{-1} and the value of the diffusion factor is 4.883×10^{-6} m^2·s^{-1}. The value of apparent activation energy in hot-air drying is between the first and second falling rate period of microwave drying. The result indicates that microwave drying is more suitable to dewatering free water and capillary water of lignite.

4. Conclusions

(1) The drying curves of Zhaotong lignite during microwave drying exhibited a warm-up period, a short constant rate period, and the first and second falling rate periods for all applied microwave drying conditions, while only one falling rate period was observed during hot-air drying. This demonstrates different heat transfer mechanisms between these two methods.

(2) The required drying time for lignite decrease by about 48% and 57% with the temperature rising from 100 °C to 140 °C and the power from 500 W to 800 W, respectively. The comparisons of the drying characteristics of lignite between microwave drying and hot-air drying indicate that microwave drying has great advantages in drying time and rate.

(3) The mathematical modeling of lignite was conducted using multiple regression analysis and the two-term exponential model is the most suitable model to describe the all microwave drying experiments, while Modified Page model was the most suitable model to describe the hot-air drying experiments. The results shows different drying kinetic mechanism between conventional and microwave drying.

(4) The drying rate and effective diffusion coefficient increase gradually with increasing temperature and microwave power levels, which indicate that it could promote moisture migration in the lignite. The Arrhenius equation was used to calculate the apparent activation energy and the results during hot-air drying is 17.078 kJ·mol^{-1} for the falling rate period. However, during microwave drying, for the first and second falling rate periods are 3.349 and 20.808 kJ·mol^{-1} at different temperatures, while it was 13.455 and 19.580 W·g^{-1} at different microwave power levels. The values of apparent activation energy are higher during the second falling rate period, which suggest that the dewatering of absorbed water is more difficult than capillary water. The value of apparent activation energy in hot-air drying is between the first and second falling rate period of microwave drying.

Author Contributions: P.Z. wrote the paper; C.L. conceived and designed the study; W.Q. carried out the literature search; J.G. and L.J. performed the the data collection and data interpretation; Z.H. and S.J. analyzed the figures and tables; R.R. contributed performed the the data collection.

Funding: The authors acknowledge the financial supports from the National Natural Science Foundation of China (CN) (no. 51504217), the National Natural Science Foundation of China—Yunnan Joint Fund Project of China (no. U1402274), the Natural Science Foundation of Yunnan Province (CN) (2015FD031), and the Science Research Foundation of Yunnan Provincial Education Department (no. 2018JS306).

Conflicts of Interest: The authors declare no conflicts of interest.

Nomenclature

M	moisture (g/(g db))
W_t	the mass of sample at t (g)
$W_{d,s}$	the dry coal mass (g)
DR	the drying rate (g/(g db min))
M_t and M_{t+dt}	the moisture content at t and t + dt (g/(g db))
MR	the moisture ratio
M_0	the initial water content (g/(g db))
M_e	the moisture content at the end of the drying experiment (g/(g db))
M_{ad}	moisture content
A_{ad}	ash content
V_{ad}	volatile content
FC_{ad}	fixed carbon content
R^2	coefficient of determination
RSS	residual sum of square
χ^2	reduced Chi-Square
D_{eff}	effective diffusion coefficient ($m^2 \cdot s^{-1}$)
L	thickness of the thin-layer (m)
t	drying time (s)
D_0	diffusion factor ($m^2 \cdot s^{-1}$)
E_a	apparent activation energy ($kJ \cdot mol^{-1}$) or ($W \cdot g^{-1}$)
T	temperature of lignite (K)
R	gas constant ($kJ \cdot mol^{-1} \cdot K^{-1}$)
m	mass of sample (g)
P	microwave power levels (W)

References

1. Zhang, Y.; Jing, X.; Jing, K.; Chang, L.; Bao, W. Study on the pore structure and oxygen-containing functional groups devoting to the hydrophilic force of dewatered lignite. *Appl. Surf. Sci.* **2015**, *324*, 90–98. [CrossRef]
2. Feng, L.; Yuan, C.; Mao, L.; Yan, C.; Jiang, X.; Liu, J.; Liu, X. Water occurrence in lignite and its interaction with coal structure. *Fuel* **2018**, *219*, 288–295. [CrossRef]
3. Feng, L.I.; Liu, X.; Song, L.; Wang, X.; Zhang, Y.; Cui, T.; Tang, H. The effect of alkali treatment on some physico–chemical properties of xilinhaote lignite. *Powder Technol.* **2013**, *247*, 19–23. [CrossRef]
4. Li, Y.; Zhao, H.; Song, Q.; Wang, X.; Shu, X. Influence of critical moisture content in lignite dried by two methods on its physicochemical properties during oxidation at low temperature. *Fuel* **2018**, *211*, 27–37. [CrossRef]
5. Liu, M.; Wang, C.; Han, X.; Li, G.; Chong, D.; Yan, J. Lignite drying with solar energy: Thermodynamic analysis and case study. *Dry. Technol.* **2017**, *35*, 1117–1129. [CrossRef]
6. Potter, O.E.; Beeby, C.J.; Fernando, W.J.N.; Ho, P. Drying brown coal in steam-heated, steam-fluidized beds. *Dry. Technol.* **1983**, *2*, 219–234. [CrossRef]
7. Agarwal, P.K.; Genetti, W.E.; Lee, Y.Y. Coupled drying and devolatilization of wet coal in fluidized beds. *Chem. Eng. Sci.* **1986**, *41*, 2373–2383. [CrossRef]
8. Bergins, C.; Hulston, J.; Strauss, K.; Chaffee, A.L. Mechanical/thermal dewatering of lignite. Part 3: Physical properties and pore structure of mte product coals. *Fuel* **2007**, *86*, 3–16. [CrossRef]

9. Hulston, J.; Favas, G.; Chaffee, A.L. Physico-chemical properties of loy yang lignite dewatered by mechanical thermal expression. *Fuel* **2005**, *84*, 1940–1948. [CrossRef]
10. Wu, J.; Liu, J.; Xu, Z.; Wang, Z.; Zhou, J.; Cen, K. Chemical and structural changes in ximeng lignite and its carbon migration during hydrothermal dewatering. *Fuel* **2015**, *148*, 139–144. [CrossRef]
11. Liu, J.; Wu, J.; Zhu, J.; Wang, Z.; Zhou, J.; Cen, K. Removal of oxygen functional groups in lignite by hydrothermal dewatering: An experimental and dft study. *Fuel* **2016**, *178*, 85–92. [CrossRef]
12. Fu, B.A.; Chen, M.Q.; Huang, Y.W.; Luo, H.F. Combined effects of additives and power levels on microwave drying performance of lignite thin layer. *Dry. Technol.* **2017**, *35*, 227–239. [CrossRef]
13. Metaxas, A.C.; Meredith, R.J. *Industrial Microwave Heating*; The Institution of Engineering and Technology: London, UK, 2008; Volume 4.
14. Binner, E.; Lester, E.; Kingman, S.; Dodds, C.; Robinson, J.; Wu, T.; Wardle, P.; Mathews, J.P. A review of microwave coal processing. *J. Microw. Power Electromagn. Energy* **2016**, *48*, 35–60. [CrossRef]
15. Metaxas, A.C. Microwave heating. *Power Eng. J.* **1991**, *5*, 237–247. [CrossRef]
16. Pickles, C.A.; Gao, F.; Kelebek, S. Microwave drying of a low-rank sub-bituminous coal. *Miner. Eng.* **2014**, *62*, 31–42. [CrossRef]
17. Song, Z.; Yao, L.; Jing, C.; Zhao, X.; Wang, W.; Ma, C. Drying behavior of lignite under microwave heating. *Dry. Technol.* **2017**, *35*, 433–443. [CrossRef]
18. Koné, K.Y.; Druon, C.; Gnimpieba, E.Z.; Delmotte, M.; Duquenoy, A.; Laguerre, J.C. Power density control in microwave assisted air drying to improve quality of food. *J. Food Eng.* **2013**, *119*, 750–757. [CrossRef]
19. Grigory, T.; Peter, V. Microwave wood modification technology and its applications. *For. Prod. J.* **2010**, *60*, 173–182.
20. Zhao, P.; Zhong, L.; Zhao, Y.; Luo, Z. Comparative studies on the effect of mineral matter on physico-chemical properties, inherent moisture and drying kinetics of chinese lignite. *Energy Convers. Manag.* **2015**, *93*, 197–204. [CrossRef]
21. Zhu, J.-F.; Liu, J.-Z.; Yuan, S.; Cheng, J.; Liu, Y.; Wang, Z.-H.; Zhou, J.-H.; Cen, K.-F. Effect of microwave irradiation on the grinding characteristics of ximeng lignite. *Fuel Process. Technol.* **2016**, *147*, 2–11. [CrossRef]
22. Williams, O.; Eastwick, C.; Kingman, S.; Giddings, D.; Lormor, S.; Lester, E. Investigation into the applicability of bond work index (bwi) and hardgrove grindability index (hgi) tests for several biomasses compared to colombian la loma coal. *Fuel* **2015**, *158*, 379–387. [CrossRef]
23. Lester, E.; Kingman, S.; Dodds, C.; Patrick, J. The potential for rapid coke making using microwave energy. *Fuel* **2006**, *85*, 2057–2063. [CrossRef]
24. Binner, E.; Mediero-Munoyerro, M.; Huddle, T.; Kingman, S.; Dodds, C.; Dimitrakis, G.; Robinson, J.; Lester, E. Factors affecting the microwave coking of coals and the implications on microwave cavity design. *Fuel Process. Technol.* **2014**, *125*, 8–17. [CrossRef]
25. Zhu, J.-F.; Liu, J.-Z.; Wu, J.-H.; Cheng, J.; Zhou, J.-H.; Cen, K.-F. Thin-layer drying characteristics and modeling of ximeng lignite under microwave irradiation. *Fuel Process. Technol.* **2015**, *130*, 62–70. [CrossRef]
26. Li, C.; Liao, J.-J.; Yin, Y.; Mo, Q.; Chang, L.-P.; Bao, W.-R. Kinetic analysis on the microwave drying of different forms of water in lignite. *Fuel Process. Technol.* **2018**, *176*, 174–181. [CrossRef]
27. Fu, B.A.; Chen, M.Q.; Song, J.J. Investigation on the microwave drying kinetics and pumping phenomenon of lignite spheres. *Appl. Therm. Eng.* **2017**, *124*, 371–380. [CrossRef]
28. Jiang, Y.; Liu, B.; Peng, J.; Zhang, L. Dielectric properties and microwave heating of molybdenite concentrate at 2.45 ghz frequency. *J. Beijing Inst. Technol.* **2018**, *27*, 83–91.
29. Page, G.E. Factors Influencing the Maximum Rates of Air Drying Shelled Corn in Thin Layers. Master's Thesis, Purdue University, West Lafayette, IN, USA, 1949.
30. Zhang, Q.; Litchfield, J.B. An optimization of intermittemt corn drying in a laboratory scale thin layer dryer. *Dry. Technol.* **1991**, *9*, 383–395. [CrossRef]
31. Overhults, D.G.; White, G.M.; Hamilton, H.E.; Ross, I.J. Drying soybeans with heated air. *Am. Soc. Agric. Eng. Trans. ASAE* **1973**, *16*, 112–113. [CrossRef]
32. Diamante, L.M.; Munro, P.A. Mathematical modelling of hot air drying of sweet potato slices. *Int. J. Food Sci. Technol.* **2010**, *26*, 99–109. [CrossRef]
33. Henderson, S.M. Progress in developing the thin layer drying equation. *Trans. ASAE* **1974**, *17*, 1167–1168. [CrossRef]

34. Rahman, M.S.; Perera, C.O.; Thebaud, C. Desorption isotherm and heat pump drying kinetics of peas. *Food Res. Int.* **1997**, *30*, 485–491. [CrossRef]
35. Sharafeldeen, Y.I.; Blaisdell, J.L.; Hamdy, M.Y. A model for ear-corn drying. *Trans. ASAE* **1980**, *23*, 1261–1265. [CrossRef]
36. O'Callaghan, J.R.; Menzies, D.J.; Bailey, P.H. Digital simulation of agricultural drier performance. *J. Agric. Eng. Res.* **1971**, *16*, 223–244. [CrossRef]
37. Ayensu, A. Dehydration of food crops using a solar dryer with convective heat flow. *Sol. Energy* **1997**, *59*, 121–126. [CrossRef]
38. Liu, Q.; Bakker-Arkema, F.W. Stochastic modelling of grain drying: Part 2. Model development. *J. Agric. Eng. Res.* **1997**, *66*, 275–280. [CrossRef]
39. Westerman, P.W.; White, G.M.; Ross, I.J. Relative humidity effect on the high-temperature drying of shelled corn. *Trans. ASAE* **1973**, *16*, 1136–1139. [CrossRef]
40. Chhinnan, M.S. Evaluation of selected mathematical models for describing thin-layer drying of in-shell pecans. *Trans. ASAE* **1984**, *27*, 0610–0615. [CrossRef]
41. Karathanos, V.T. Determination of water content of dried fruits by drying kinetics. *J. Food Eng.* **1999**, *39*, 337–344. [CrossRef]
42. Yagcioglu, A.; Degirmencioglu, A.; Cagatay, F. Drying characteristics of laurel leaves under different drying conditions. In Proceedings of the 7th International Congress on Agricultural Mechanization and Energy, Adana, Turkey, 26–27 May 2002; Bascetincelik, A., Ed.; Faculty of Agriculture, Çukurova University: Adana, Turkey, 2002; pp. 565–569.
43. Wang, C.Y.; Singh, R.P. *Single Layer Drying Equation for Rough Rice*; American Society of Agricultural Engineers: St. Joseph, MI, USA, 1978.
44. Kassem, A.S. Comparative studies on thin layer drying models for wheat. In Proceedings of the 13th International Congress on Agricultural Engineering, Rabat, Morocco, 2–6 February 1998; Volume 6, pp. 2–6.
45. Verma, L.R.; Bucklin, R.A.; Endan, J.B.; Wratten, F.T. Effects of drying air parameters on rice drying models. *Trans. ASAE* **1985**, *28*, 296–301. [CrossRef]
46. Midilli, A.; Kucuk, H.; Yapar, Z. A new model for single-layer drying. *Dry. Technol.* **2002**, *20*, 1503–1513. [CrossRef]
47. Fu, B.A.; Chen, M.Q. Thin-layer drying kinetics of lignite during hot air forced convection. *Chem. Eng. Res. Des.* **2015**, *102*, 416–428. [CrossRef]
48. Song, Z.; Yao, L.; Jing, C.; Zhao, X.; Wang, W.; Mao, Y.; Ma, C. Experimental study on the characteristics of ignition during microwave drying of lignite. *Energy Technol.* **2016**, *4*, 1077–1083. [CrossRef]
49. Tahmasebi, A.; Yu, J.; Han, Y.; Zhao, H.; Bhattacharya, S. A kinetic study of microwave and fluidized-bed drying of a chinese lignite. *Chem. Eng. Res. Des.* **2014**, *92*, 54–65. [CrossRef]
50. Kara, C.; Doymaz, İ. Effective moisture diffusivity determination and mathematical modelling of drying curves of apple pomace. *Heat Mass Transf.* **2015**, *51*, 983–989. [CrossRef]
51. Li, H.; Chang, Q.; Gao, R.; Dai, Z.; Chen, X.; Yu, G.; Wang, F. Thin-layer drying characteristics and modeling of lignite under supercritical carbon dioxide extraction and the evolution of pore structure and reactivity. *Fuel Process. Technol.* **2018**, *170*, 1–12. [CrossRef]

MDPI

St. Alban-Anlage 66

4052 Basel

Switzerland

Tel. +41 61 683 77 34

Fax +41 61 302 89 18

www.mdpi.com

Processes Editorial Office

E-mail: processes@mdpi.com

www.mdpi.com/journal/processes